The Author

Born in 1898, the author qualified as a junior navigator in the First World War; he served in the Mediterranean and Atlantic theatres, and was torpedoed three times. He later obtained Master Mariner and Extra Master Mariners Certificates in succession, after which he was to be appointed Junior Hydrographic Surveyor to the Mersey Docks and Harbour Board in 1930.

He was appointed Hydrographic Surveyor in charge at the Southampton Harbour Board in 1934. During the Second World War he was responsible for research in mine location, and became Surveying Officer attached to the C. & C. Portsmouth prior to the Normandy invasion in 1943.

After the War he resumed his position at Southampton, and is now in private practice as a consultant.

Tides

Tides

by
Commander D. H. Macmillan
M.B.E., R.N.R., F.R.I.C.S., F.I.N.

Chartered Hydrographic Surveyor

Master Mariner (Extra) and Marine
Consultant

NEW YORK
AMERICAN ELSEVIER PUBLISHING COMPANY, INC.

© D. H. MACMILLAN, 1966

First Published 1966

AMERICAN ELSEVIER PUBLISHING COMPANY, INC.

52 Vanderbilt Avenue
New York 17, New York

LIBRARY OF CONGRESS CATALOGUE CARD NUMBER: 66-23190

Made and printed in Great Britain by
F. J. Parsons, Ltd., London, Folkestone, Hastings

Acknowledgements

I SHOULD like to express my indebtedness to the Admiralty Manual of Tides (referred to in the text and captions as A.M.T.) a standard work, and to its distinguished and principal author, Dr. A. T. Doodson, F.R.S., who as first Director of the now famous Liverpool Tidal Institute has played a major part in the development of tidal reasearch during the last half century. I am particularly grateful to Dr. Doodson for many valuable suggestions, corrections and generous assistance, although of course he is not to be held in any way responsible for my opinions and conclusions.

Grateful acknowledgement is also due to the following persons and institutions whose kind collaboration has alone made this work possible but who are of course not responsible either for the opinions and conclusions expressed or the accuracy of the information appearing:

The Hydrographer of the Navy; Cdr. D. Gordon, Superintendent of the Tidal Branch (Admiralty Hydrographic Dept.); The Superintendent H.M. Nautical Almanac Office; The Controller H.M. Stationary Office, for permission to use, reproduce, and quote from official publications e.g. Admiralty Charts and Manual of Tides (Abbr.A.M.T.); The Pergamon Press for permission to reproduce diagrams from PHYSICAL OCEANOGRAPHY, Part II (Defant); The Southampton Harbour Board; Frances N. Clark, Supervisor of the California State Fisheries Laboratory; The United States Coast and Geodetic Survey; The Department of Naval Service, Ottawa, Canada; Cambridge University Press; Dr. Rossiter and Mr. Lennon of the Liverpool Tidal Institute; Mr. H. R. Potter of the Trent River Board; Monsieur X Picot de Moras, French Consul at Southampton, also M. M. Le Garrec of the Consulate; The Chef de Services of Electricité de France, for details of the Rance Installation; Messrs. Kelvin Hughes and in particular Mr. A. J. Wood for valuable information on recent developments in current meters and photographs; The Canadian Information Service and the kind collaboration of Mrs. J. D. Swanston of that service; Mr. N. Webber, Lecturer in Civil Engineering at Southampton University; Mr. Van de Wetering for the Dutch Tidal curves; Mr. T. Richardson for most of the line drawings; Mr. J. R. Brogan, F.R.I.C.S. for reading and checking page proofs; My Wife who typed the entire manuscript and checked all galley proofs; Also to the many unmentioned collaborators to whom I am most grateful.

TO MY WIFE, UNA

Contents

CONTENTS

8

Foreword

by Sir Edmund Irving, K.B.E., C.B.
Hydrographer of the Royal Navy, 1960 - 66

A great number of manuals and text books have been written on the theory of tides but most of them are too advanced to be easily understood by the student.

In general the mariner requires little more than the times and heights of high and low water, on the hourly heights of the tide and these can be readily extracted from tide tables.

However there are those who will wish to have a basic understanding of the principles of tidal theories and Commander Macmillan has filled this want in this revised expanded and modernized version of his earlier work published in 1952.

His lifetime of practical experience lends weight to his words which give a simple and intelligible explanation to enable the beginner to grasp the fundamental facts without fear or difficulty.

CHAPTER ONE

The pulse of the earth

THE GREAT seas of the world, which form the oceanic film that covers two-thirds of the surface of our planet, are never really at rest, despite frequent manifestations of outward calm. Underlying all the irregular disturbances, which on occasions lash their surfaces into awe-inspiring tumults, there exist subtle and regular pulsations, the explanations of which are to most people even yet shrouded in no inconsiderable mystery.

The behaviour of the oceans to the observer is not unlike that of the human body. Outwardly its movements are often irregular and spasmodic, being dependent upon mental activities, relatively unpredictable, yet underneath, the close observer discerns the rhythmic pulsations of the heart transmitted throughout the entire body by the essential activity of the streams of life blood.

The ancient civilizations of the near and middle East have contributed little to our understanding of the tidal movements of the oceans, very largely because their situations were upon the shores of the Mediterranean or Great Sea, wherein the vertical oscillations are no greater in amplitude than one foot or so, and of little practical significance. To such people the dominant phenomena of the seas were rather those of storm surge and flood, sometimes occasioned by prevailing gales, great rivers in spate and drought, shattering earthquakes or perhaps a combination of all. The history of the Deluge and legend of Atlantis are indicative of their experience in the irregular wellings and declensions of the somewhat limited great waters, in which the destinies of the ancient peoples of the Mediterranean were set.

EARLY IDEAS ABOUT TIDES

Yet there was a somewhat exclusive school of ancient mariners, the Phoenicians, with their Hebrew and Greek shipmates, who were steeped in the truly scientific lore of the philosopher-scientists of Miletus—and, who, greatly daring, had passed through the pillars of Hercules into the unknown sea towards the sunset, and by rough cross-staff latitudes found their way to the Sacred Isles of Ierne and Albion in their quest for minerals and precious stones.

The search for treasure was for the hardiest and most able navigators among them, for the prevailing westerly winds and gales were adverse to their venture and even in their havens of refuge they discovered daily variations of sea level, which grim tales of the disasters of predecessors had caused them to respect. Then, as now, to be ignorant of Dame Nature is to court a deadly foe, whereas knowledge of her decrees guarantees her welcome. Off the French coasts they would encounter large and varying tidal "ranges," or differences of level between High Water and preceding or succeeding Low Waters, of up to 30 feet, or five of their ancient fathoms, or "hand spreadings." Off Penzeance, or near the Ictis of the ancients, St. Michael's Mount, a good fifteen feet of rise and fall would make them cautious in seeking an entrance or anchorage in the precarious harbours of the French and British coasts.

From local fishermen they would discover that at the times of full and new moon there came the Live-water or Springing-water when after the full flood, water level fell low enough to expose the greatest beach area making it worth while to take their parties and carts to gather crabs, mussells, and sea foods so essential for their sustenance. The fishermen would also tell them that when the moon was showing half its disc at the quarters, the tide would move little in level or stream and so they called it the time of Dead-water.

From the earliest ages tidal phenomena have been of vital importance to those who fish for a livelihood, and the aspect and size of the moon's disc and diameter at Spring Tides would indicate their best prospects.

Herodotus (450 B.C.) records tidal phenomena in the Red Sea, the eastern terminus of the ships of Tarshish. Himilco the Carthaginian admiral who visited British shores about 500 B.C. would not fail to note the strong ebb and flow off the British coasts.

Aristotle (350 B.C.) summarising ancient sea lore, says: "It is even said that many ebbings and risings of the sea always come round with the moon and upon certain fixed days."

The Greek navigator-scientist Pytheas (325 B.C.), sailed from Marseilles to Britain and is said to have been the first author to note what is known as phase inequality, or the alteration in tidal range between Springs and Neaps, and also to measure accurately the height of the tide. In exasperatingly scarce fragments from the writer Diodorus Siculus and others we learn of the close attention paid by this remarkable explorer to ancient Britain, including his description of the strong Spring tidal streams of the Pentland Firth.

Strabo (54 B.C.) also collating Phoenicean and Greek sea lore, describes tidal movement around the coasts of Spain and Portugal, Italy, the Persian Gulf, Britain and Denmark.

It is somewhat naive of the great Caesar to state apologetically, in his De Bello Gallico, that the disaster to his war galleys (which were hauled up on the British shores somewhat injudiciously at Neaps or dead-water, and devastated at Springs) was due to the fact that none of his people knew about the relation between such high tides and the full moon! This apologia must have been of a piece with the exaggerations about those "ignorant savages", the ancient Britons, who, with the whole Phoenicean, Gallic and Greek maritime world were fully cognizant of the broad outlines of tidal phenomena in relation to the moon's aspect in size and shape. Military and naval failures no doubt required some explanation from so great a Roman, and it seems clear that what might be poor excuses in Carthage and the Piraeus would not be without their power of conviction in the Roman Senate.

The Roman historian Pliny (A.D. 23-79) in his Natural History, summarizes the tidal lore of his time in some detail, and represents contemporary knowledge in an empirical fashion, most of it, no doubt, learnt in some agony by Roman military experimenters in the seas of the West. He notes for a number of places, the rough fixed relationship between the time of full moon and the occurrence of high water, and that the difference in the amplitude or range between high and low water is least when the moon shows half her disc, and greatest when she shows either her whole orb at full, or only her slender crescent at new. Pliny records, quite accurately, the fact that tidal high water levels at new or full moon tend to reach their highest at the times of the equinoxes (when the sun is over the equator), rather than at the solstices (when the moon is farthest north or farthest south of the equator).

The Scandinavian sagas frequently mention, but do not attempt to explain, tidal phenomena.

The word "tide" itself derives from the Anglo-Saxon "tyd" which actually means "seasons" in a general sense. Amongst the sea peoples of the West the seasons of the moon could not fail to be associated in their minds with the hydraulic pulses around their shores.

The Venerable Bede (A.D. 672-735), as well as recounting the general features of tidal behaviour, noted by the ancients, and culled no doubt from their writings to some extent, notices the progress of the tidal undulation from north to south down the North Sea coasts of Britain, a fact which his Anglo-Saxon contemporaries must have observed and utilized.

It is remarkable that during the Middle Ages the moderately sound scientific methods of the Milesian philosophers and their followers, from Pythagoras and Thales to Eratosthenes, together with much subtle nautical knowledge, became increasingly unknown, and the grotesque caricatures of much physical theorizing by Aristotle perpetuated this state of affairs until the Renaissance and Reformation broke the slumber of true science. This is eminently true of tidal science and perhaps we may say that the possible course of British history was (in at least one case) fortunately, if accidently, altered by such ignorance. In October, A.D. 1216, King John, when marching from Lynn towards Wisbech was fatally surprised by the flood tide and lost part of his army and all his baggage and treasure in the fords of the Wash. The psychological effect of such an unexpected event caused him not unnaturally, to become ill of rage and vexation of spirit, and he died a week later.

One ancient writer has said that the tides and their behaviour can be regarded as the tomb of human curiosity, but it is certain that knowledge of their general behaviour and the use of rough rules for their prediction, are indispensable for such a maritime people as our own.   The scheduling of the great liners of today, drawing up to 40 feet, for terminal ports with Spring low water depths at 35 feet, or thereabouts, demands a precise knowledge of high water and intermediate levels if safe clearances are to be enjoyed.

Such accuracy in prediction, which is now attainable to a matter of a few inches under normal weather conditions, has only been made possible by the great increase in factual knowledge about the universe which followed upon the awakening of Western Europe at the Renaissance and is still proceeding apace.

TIDAL TIMES

The names of those men of science who have contributed to the precise modern methods for tidal prediction are many, but it is interesting to give an ancient table for the time of High Water or "flod at london brigge," produced by the Abbot of St. Albans in 1213, relating the moon's age in days from new moon to the times of high water.

Aetus Lunae (in days)	Hours (Time of day)	Minutes
1	3	48
2	4	36
3	5	24
—	—	—
—	—	—
30	3	0

This table is included in "Codex Cottonianus Julius DVII," the MS. of which is available in the British Museum, and shows the time of High Water corresponding to the number of days after new moon.

For a port in Western Europe, the actual times of high and low water at Spring tides, which occur at new and full moon, are approximately constant.   As an ability to predict the hours of high and low water is of importance to seamen, an empirical knowledge of such times (known as the local "establishment") was arrived at very early. Such data in fact, appear in the famous Catalan Atlas prepared for Charles V in 1375, but some information was obviously available long before this compilation.

Certainly there were many outstanding tidal mysteries at the time when the Spanish Armada essayed its perilous attack on the British coasts in the sixteenth century despite the opening up of the seas of the world to the seamen venturers of those days.

Whilst the rise and fall of the tide or "range" between successive high and low waters seemed to vary considerably even around the British coasts, the progressive movement of the oceanic undulations along the coasts of the continents could not easily be systematically observed in those times.

At many localities elsewhere in the world, the normal semi-diurnal tides occurred with the same ranges, twice a day at roughly $12\frac{1}{2}$ hour intervals. At others, however, on some occasions the main tidal rise occurred *once* a day only with perhaps a very small tidal rise following $12\frac{1}{2}$ hours later or sometimes even none at all. In many places, therefore, only one tide a day was apparent. At other places in the world, at about monthly intervals, tidal ranges seemed to be larger when the moon appeared larger in diameter than on other occasions. Again it had been noticed, as we have said before, that at the equinoxes tidal ranges tended to be larger than at other seasons. It was evident that there must be some general underlying causes for these varying phenomena and incidentally it was quite impossible to attribute any of them to the sun until the first key was discovered to unlock the mystery and unify the increase in knowledge of the grand principles involved.

In the seventeenth century the great increase in scientific research resulting from the opening of the book of the heavens to astronomers, with their exact knowledge of the earth and the heliocentric system in which it moved, paved the way for the most remarkable galaxy of savants the world had hitherto seen at any one time, and most of them were Britons.

Of these the names of Sir Isaac Newton, Bacon, Descartes, Wallis, Flamsteed and Halley are prominent, but that of the great Newton must take precedence over all in that he revealed the gravitational forces controlling the vast universe. He was the real originator of that tidal science which now rests on secure foundations. His justifiable exultation at identifying the force which caused the apple's fall with that which keeps the moon in her orbit, was only exceeded by his conviction that the law of gravitation exerted between the earth, sun and moon, explained the tidal mysteries of the ancients.

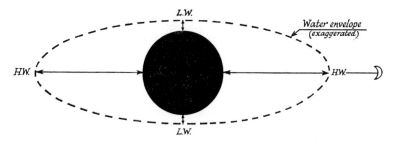

Fig. I. I   Equilibrium envelope acted upon by tractive forces

Newton was able to show that the attractive forces of the moon would vary over the surface of the earth and that the forces on the side nearest the moon would be greater than the average forces and so would tend to move the water towards the moon; whereas the forces on the opposite side of the earth would be less then the average forces and so the water would tend to move away from the moon. In an ocean completely covering the earth, and of great depth, the water would be heaped up on opposite sides, towards and away from the moon, so that the water would be symmetrically disposed round the earth in relation to the moon. Similarly, the sun would tend to give like effects related to itself, and when sun and moon were in line their effects would add together as at springs. Any island rotating through the fluid envelope would thus experience changes of high and low water. The main features of the tides were explained in this way.

On such an ocean-covered earth the shape and disposition of the oceanic film would be determined by the relative positions of the sun and moon, and their distances would also play a part. Calculations showed that if the universal law of gravitation were

B

as stated by Newton, varying according to the masses of the attracting bodies and inversely as the squares of their distances, then the solar tides, on the average, would be rather less than half the lunar tides, and this indication was confirmed. A complete knowledge of the astronomical regime would thus solve the problem of the tides.

ASTRONOMICAL FACTORS

The following astronomical considerations would on this assumption greatly affect tidal behaviour:

(i) The sun and moon's varying phase relations throughout the lunar month.

(ii) The variations in the moon's distance from the earth. She is nearest at perigee, farthest away at apogee. This cycle is slightly less than the lunar month.

(iii) The sun's variation in orbital distance from the earth which changes annually from its nearest at perihelion to its farthest at aphelion.

(iv) The positions of the sun and moon in declination, being the latitudes in which they were overhead.

(v) Long-period cyclic variations in the moon's declination.

In other words a true knowledge of the movements of the sun and moon would enable the shape of the "plastic" oceanic film to be calculated, using the graviational rule.

Such applications of astronomical and gravitational knowledge certainly gave a rough qualitative explanation of much that was mysterious by postulating an ideal ocean and regarding it as "plastically" moulded by gravitational forces and rotated through by an observer situated upon an insular protuberance. The tidal undulation was assumed to be a static mound in equilibrium through which the earth rotated. But mysteries remained.

SOME OBSERVED DISCREPANCIES

The proportion of the solar tide to the lunar did not appear to be the same in all oceans, although the characteristics corresponded in most cases with the general principles assumed and oceanic islands recorded an approximate rise and fall of about two feet above and below mean sea level as expected. Yet the summit of the tidal undulation was not always found to be directly under the moon, or in other words it was not high water locally when the moon bore north or south, or was on the meridian. The summit often lagged by many hours behind the position with the moon overhead.

This was attributed to the fact that the uninterrupted ocean was a theoretical dream only, or at best an "ocean of reference" for estimating qualitative effects. In practice the tidal undulation is obliged to follow a circuitous path; also there are many hydraulic factors which cause it to diminish and increase in range, the former perhaps by dissipation of energy through friction and the latter by decrease in section as in converging estuaries or by barriers at right angles to the course of the tidal wave. For example, Atlantic oceanic tides rise and fall one or two feet above and below mean sea level respectively, yet in the Bay of Fundy the range is nearly 50 feet and in the Bristol Channel at Avonmouth attains to over 40 feet.

The equilibrium theory of the great Newton, which we have roughly indicated, could not precisely explain the relation between the facts observed in tidal levels and the dynamical movement of the waters involved, but it served as a guide to the reduction of tidal observations.

Elaborate calculations of various recorded mean levels in connection with the occurrence of astronomical features led to practical methods of prediction. Methods were kept secret and even handed down from father to son up to the end of the nineteenth century.

For general results these predictions were well within the limits required for the shallow-draught vessels then involved, but it is well that tidal science has at last reached precision more fitting to the requirements of our times.

TIDAL TERMS

A few of the more elementary tidal definitions are now given: *Datum* is a plane from which the heights of tide are measured; it is usually fixed so that few tides fall below it. All heights are referred to this.

Rise is the height of high water on the adopted scale, the height being measured from a so-called datum, which is an arbitrarily fixed plane.

Range is the difference in level between the height of high water and height of the next succeeding or last preceding low water.

Mean High Water Springs (*M.H.W.S.*) and *Mean High Water Neaps* (*M.H.W.N.*) are the heights of high water at Springs and Neaps respectively, averaged over a long period.

Mean Low Water Springs (*M.L.W.S.*) and *Mean Low Water Neaps* (*M.L.W.N.*) are the levels of low water at springs and neaps respectively averaged over a long period.

The datum of soundings on nautical charts is often taken as approximately the level of M.L.W.S., representing the level below which the tide seldom falls.

Mean (*or Half*) *Tide Level* (*M.T.L.*) is the mean of mean high and low waters taken over a long-period. This includes shallow water effects and is not the same as mean sea level.

Mean Sea Level (*M.S.L.*) is the average level of the sea above datum, calculated from a long series of equally spaced observations.

Semi-Diurnal Tide—One where high waters occur twice daily at intervals averaging 12.4 hours.

Diurnal Tide—One where high waters occur once daily at intervals averaging 24.8 hours.

Time of High Water is the moment of high water at which the highest level is attained and after which the level falls.

Lunitidal Interval is the interval of time between the transit of the moon over the meridian and the following high water time.

Tidal Establishment of a Place is the average and nearly constant time interval between the time of the moon's crossing the meridian of the place on the day of new or full moon, and the time of the following high water at the place where the tides are of a semi-diurnal character. This is the mean lunitidal interval on the days of the full moon or change to new moon and is sometimes abbreviated as H.W.F. and C. The term has now become obsolete.

There is a corresponding quantity on the low waters sometimes abbreviated as L.W.F. and C.

Phase Inequality is the variation in tidal range *or* lunitidal interval throughout the lunar month due to the different dispositions of the moon from the sun throughout the lunar phases.

Age of the Tide is the interval between new or full moon and the following springs where the tide is semi-diurnal.

Syzygies—The instant when the sun and moon are in opposition or conjunction; that is, at full or new moon.

Quadrature—The instant when the sun and moon are at right angles to each other as measured at the centre of the earth, that is, at the first and third quarters.

GROWTH OF ACCURATE TIDAL KNOWLEDGE IN MODERN TIMES

The gravitational principles elaborated by Newton in his Principia opened the way to further scientific conceptions in advance of his equilibrium theory, which assumed an uninterrupted ocean covering a sphere. His grand principle that all forces in the universe tend to a state of equilibrium or balance of forces, did not take into account those modern concepts which also consider the dynamical behaviour of fluids once set in motion.

If in such an uninterrupted ocean, seas are continuously to build up immediately under and also opposite the moon, and consequently to become shallower over an earth-encircling zone—where she is either rising or setting—the movement of the water must also be governed by the usual laws of hydraulic motion. Consequently, factors involving the behaviour of fluids in motion had to be considered, and the whole matter dealt with where necessary as a problem in dynamics.

As will be shown elsewhere a wave generated by tidal or other forces is a storehouse of energy, and a tidal wave is fundamentally a result of the earth's rotation. Therefore, the varying effects of the earth's rotation and the gyroscopic phenomena arising out of it must not be overlooked.

The unparalleled range and breadth of Newton's brilliant analyses of physical phenomena are enough to fill the lives of a dozen truly great men, but it has been left to others to develop in tidal science the principles he so ably initiated.

Soon after Newton's death, Bernoulli, a French scientist, won an award in the course of which he formulated his famous

21

equation dealing with hydraulic motion. This, after modification, has proved a useful key in explaining many complex factors in tidal motion. Bernoulli's theorem is really an extension of the Law of Conservation of Energy and shows that along a streamline the sum of the fluid pressure intensity, and the kinetic and potential energies per unit mass, is a constant. The theorem refers to steady motion, but tidal scientists have adapted it to an imaginary observer stationed at a particular part of the wave and observing the relative hydraulic flow from this viewpoint.

The famous Laplace (1749-1827) continued research along similar lines and it has been claimed with some justice, that his dynamical theories are complementary to the equilibrium concepts of Newton, and in fact, are a logical development from the Principia. Laplace, in addition to solving equations of motion on an "ideal" rotating earth, was the first to separate the various cyclic variations of the sun and moon, in distance and declination, into a series of constituents which he associated with fictitious tide-raising "satellites" whose movements are less complex than those of the actual sun and moon. Laplace thus paved the way for systematic harmonic methods of analysis and prediction, which assume the tidal curve to be a summation of the tidal constituents corresponding to such separate and fictitious astronomical "satellites."

Lord Kelvin (1824-1907) systematized this method, which can be solved by mechanical devices. The effect is that the constituents of the equilibrium tide are replaced by corresponding tidal constituents with the same period and with phase-lags and amplitudes deduced from observation.

It must be emphasized that it is not yet possible to deduce local tides and their constituents with absolute precision by purely theoretical expedients, but theory gives the basis for analysis and for the tidal constituents.

The names of Sir George Darwin and Lord Rayleigh are further links in the chain of continuing discovery, but it was not until the twentieth century that the theory of hydraulic "resonance" in oceans, seas, estuaries and gulfs, and the effects of the rotation of the earth on moving fluids, were fully recognized.

In the "resonance" theory oceanic areas are regarded very much as one might consider a series of pendulums of differing lengths, suspended from a rod. Each has a period appropriate to its length. If we give to all the pendulums an equal impulse every five seconds, those whose period is equal to, or a multiple of, five seconds, will "resonate" and build up rhythmically to the periodic disturbing force. Others will resonate in "beats" only when successive applications bring about a synchronization. In other cases there will be little opportunity for resonance. So with seas and oceans. Each has its fixed natural period of oscillation and if this resonates with the semi-diurnal or other astronomical disturbing cycle, the build-up will be considerable. Similarly—even in small seas—the resonance will become apparent at the time of critical coincidences over cycles which are related to their natural periods of oscillation.

Shapes, depths, boundaries, and the direction of the major axes of such oceanic areas, will determine their natural periods of oscillation. Where the circumstances are favourable, circular movements of tidal undulations occur, increasing in range away from and around places where sea level is unvaried. These arise from complex causes consequent upon the rotation of the earth.

Added to all this, we must remember that the seas are, as the book of Genesis suggests, mostly interconnected or "gathered into one," and there are hydraulic interactions which are yet little understood. Broadly speaking it is now believed that the tidal waves in the great oceans are less dependent upon each other than was hitherto thought. Gulfs and estuaries have "stationary wave" periods which react to the oceanic waves off the entrances in accordance with the theory of resonance, as will be shown later.

The phenomenon of rotatory tidal steams has to a large degree yielded up its secrets, yet whilst we can predict tidal behaviour with as much accuracy as can reasonably be desired, there are many physical mysteries which our present state of tidal theory cannot satisfactorily solve, although steady progress in research is being made.

As the Admiralty Manual of Tides indicates, when we can explain tidal behaviour quantitatively without reference to observation, the ultimate knowledge of tidal phenomena and origins will be in sight.

We now know precisely the astronomical forces which generate the basic tidal impulses, but the behaviour of the fluid media on which they act and the irregular contours of seas and oceans introduce complexities which still evade precise computation.

The Hydrographic Department of the British Admiralty first published tables giving the predicted height of High Water in four ports in the British Isles in 1833, following them up three years later with more ports and heights as well. In 1920, High and Low Water times and heights were being computed for 28 British and 34 Colonial and Foreign ports. In 1941, the British Admiralty Tide Tables contained predictions for 133 standard ports throughout the world, with tables of constants facilitating the computation of approximate times and heights of tide at many smaller ports adjacent to Standard Ports.

Kelvin predicting machines exist at more than 15 sites throughout the civilized world, and the German Admiralty produced a number of portable machines of a rather inferior accuracy. It is a commentary on the present state of tidal prediction to state that whilst no machine can predict accurately complex shallow-water tides, it is possible by several ingenious methods to devise corrections to primary machine predictions which can, for example, give an accuracy closer than 10 minutes in time and 6 inches in height for over 90 per cent of the predictions for the Port of Liverpool. The electronic computer is now superseding the machine.

The prediction of meteorological tides is a very ambitious project but it is significant that several storm surges in the North Sea have now been computed with some precision.

BIBLIOGRAPHY

Admiralty Manual of Tides, 1941 (Abbr. A.M.T.) (Applicable to whole of book).
CAESAR—De Bello Gallico (Bk. IV-29).
STRABO—Geography (Teubner Tr.) Vol. I, p. 236.
DIODORUS SICULUS—Historical Library (London 1814).
HERODOTUS.
PLINY—Natural History.
BEDE—Ecclesiastical History.
SIR ISAAC NEWTON—Principia.
SIR GEORGE DARWIN—The Tide (1911).
MARMER—The Tide (1926).

HEIBERG—Mathematical and Physical Science in Classical Antiquity. O.U.P. 1922.

LORD KELVIN (SIR W. THOMSON)—Popular Lectures and Addresses, 1891. (Vol. III).

WHEWELL. History of the Inductive Sciences. 1837, Vol. II, p. 248 et seq.

LAPLACE—Mecanique Celeste (XIII-I).

BERNOULLI—Hydrodynamica, 1738.

CHAPTER TWO

General features of the equilibrium theory

The fundamental movements governing the tidal pulses are:

(a) The revolution of the moon in an elliptical orbit around the earth in a period of $29\frac{1}{2}$ days.

(b) The revolution of the earth in an elliptical orbit around the sun in $365\frac{1}{4}$ days.

(c) The rotation of the earth on its own axis in a period of 24 hours or one solar day.

If all these movements were in the plane of the earth's equator, tidal prediction would be greatly simplified, although this would involve alternating eclipses of sun and moon at regular fortnightly intervals. As, however, the earth's axis is set at an angle of $66\frac{1}{2}°$ to the ecliptic, or plane of the orbit around the sun, and the moon's orbit is inclined about 5° 9′ to the ecliptic, eclipses fortunately cannot exceed eight annually (see Fig. II, 1).

The sun's declination (or latitude in which it is overhead at noon) varies from $23\frac{1}{2}°$ north of the equator in summer, when it is overhead at midday in the tropic of Cancer, to $23\frac{1}{2}°$ south in winter, when it is overhead at midday in the tropic of Capricorn. (Fig. II, 2). At such times, and because the moon's orbit is inclined about 5° to the ecliptic, there are occasions, which occur every 18.6 years, when the moon's declination may reach a value of $28\frac{1}{2}°$ north or south.

The soli-lunar cycles known to the ancients as the Saros (18.03 years), and the Metonic (19 years), giving the recurrence of eclipses and the lunar phases respectively, illustrate other long period epochs bearing on tidal origins.

As the solar system moves and has its being in a universe held together by the force of universal gravitation, any two

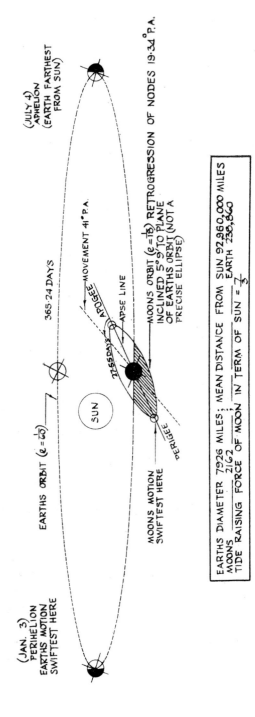

EARTHS DIAMETER 7926 MILES; MEAN DISTANCE FROM SUN 92,960,000 MILES

MOONS 2162; MEAN DISTANCE FROM SUN 92,960,000 MILES EARTH 238,860

TIDE RAISING FORCE OF MOON IN TERM OF SUN = 7/3

Fig. II, 1 Principal astronomical factors affecting tides

(JULY 4)
APHELION
(EARTH FARTHEST
FROM SUN)

RETROGRESSION OF NODES 19.34° P.A.

MOONS ORBIT (e=1/18) INCLINED 5°9' TO PLANE OF EARTHS ORBIT (NOT A PRECISE ELLIPSE)

365·24 DAYS

APOGEE MOVEMENT 41° P.A.

27·55 DAYS

APSE LINE

PERIGEE

MOONS MOTION SWIFTEST HERE

SUN

EARTHS ORBIT (e=1/60)

(JAN. 3)
PERIHELION
EARTHS MOTION
SWIFTEST HERE

27

bodies are held in a field of mutual attraction with an intensity varying in inverse proportion to the square of the distance between them. As the moon moves in an elliptical orbit with an eccentricity of $\frac{1}{18}$, the intensity of its attraction felt on the earth, disregarding rotation, will vary from least at apogee, or the position of the moon's farthest distance from the earth, to maximum at perigee when the moon's distance is least. This cycle is completed (from perigee to perigee) in 27.5 days.

Similarly the intensity of attraction by the sun felt on the earth will be least at aphelion in July, and greatest at perihelion in January.

If the earth did not rotate, its fluid envelope would adjust itself to the resultant field of gravitational force set up by the sun and moon in combination, and at any given place the lunar tide would occur twice monthly.

In gravitational fields, the attractive force between any two particles varies directly with the product of their masses and inversely as the square of the distance between them, or:

$$F \propto \frac{m \ m'}{d^2}$$

Here F is the attractive force on a line joining the centres of particles, m and m' are the masses of the particles and d is the distance between centres.

Clearly, if every particle on our earth experienced the same lunar attractive force there would be no forces causing *relative* movements of the particles.

If, however, some of the particles, or groups of them, are attracted more than other adjacent particles, a separating or differential force will move them relatively to one another.

By way of illustration, consider two locomotives proceeding in the same direction with a spring cable secured to the rear of the leading engine and to the front of the other (as in Fig. II, 3 (a)). Let X be the centre of the cable, and l the length without tension.

If both engines are proceeding say at precisely 40 m.p.h. under their own power, no tension will occur in the cable. If

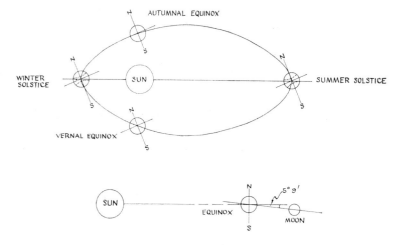

Fig. II, 2 Earth's orbit and seasons

the rear engine slows down to a speed equivalent to 30 m.p.h. when proceeding on her own, the differential speed would be 10 m.p.h. which would also be their relative and separating speed, if they were unconnected.

The result would be that each end of the cable, as measured from X, would be lengthened by the amount Y, the spring cable adjusting itself to the differential and separating force as in Fig. II, 3 (b).

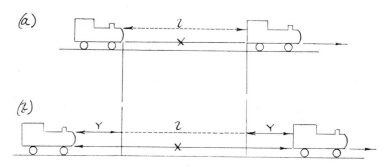

Fig. II, 3 Train analogy for differential forces

The moon's attraction on a particle of unit mass at the centre of the earth is given by:

$$g \cdot \frac{M}{E} \cdot \frac{e^2}{r^2}$$

or:

$$32.2 \times \frac{\text{moon's mass}}{\text{earth's mass}} \times \frac{(\text{distance of particle from earth's centre})^2}{(\text{distance of moon})^2}$$

As the moon's mass is $\dfrac{1}{81.5}$ that of the earth, we may roughly illustrate the differential force acting at a point X assuming the earth itself to be free of distortion (as in Fig. II, 4 Top).

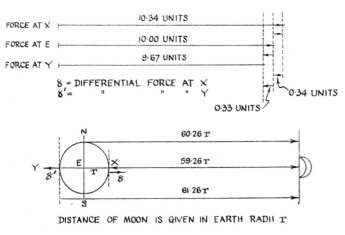

Fig. II, 4 (Top) Differential force in linear units (Bottom) In earth radii (from Introduction to Oceanography—Johnstone)

Assuming the lunar attractive force at E to be 10 units, Top Fig. II, 4 will illustrate the differential or tide-raising forces at X, E and Y respectively in linear values using a special scale of units.

At N and S in Fig. II, 4 (Bottom) a compressive differential force towards the centre E would have a value of 0.17 units.

Fig. II, 5 shows the disposition of these forces on a plane

through N Y S X. The position t illustrates the maximum horizontal resultant force along the surface of the earth which draws particles towards the line of centres.

The important thing to realize in the light of modern research is that the *horizontal,* and not the vertical, component of the differential force, has real significance in the production of tidal movements. This is called the tractive force.

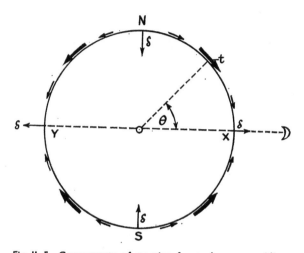

Fig. II, 5 Components of tractive force along a meridian
δ = differential force tide raising at X and Y, but to negligible degree.
t = tractive force, developed along surface of earth. Zero at N. and S., maxima
at 45°/135° from line of centres developing maximum range at X and Y.

The vertical component of the differential force is interesting in that it modifies the apparent force of gravity. For example, if the moon is directly overhead in the zenith a body will lose $\frac{1}{10,000,000}$ of its weight, approximately.

Thus, the liner Queen Mary would lose 18 pounds in weight when the moon was overhead.

We can see therefore, that at a point near t in the diagrams (Fig. II, 5 and 6) the tractive force is at a maximum, but that this diminishes to zero directly under the moon and also on the great circle plane passing through the earth's centre and normal to the line joining earth and moon centres.

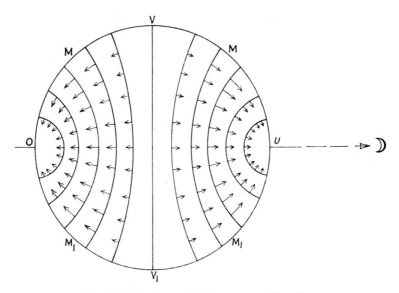

Fig. II, 6   Moon's tractive forces on earth's surface

The horizontal component of the moon's differential force or the tractive force T at any point is given by the following formula:

$$T = \frac{3}{2} g \cdot \frac{M}{E} \cdot \frac{e^3}{r^3} \sin 2\theta$$

or unconventionally:

$$T = 1.5\, g. \frac{\text{Moon's mass}}{\text{Earth's mass}} \times \frac{(\text{Earth's radius})^3}{(\text{Moon's distance})^3} \times \sin 2\theta$$

where θ is the angular distance of this point, measured at the centre of the earth, from the line of centres.

Here we note that whilst gravitational forces exerted upon particles vary inversely with the *square* of the distance, the actual tide-raising forces, depending upon the tractive force, vary inversely with the *cube* of the distance.

We may consider the sun's effects along exactly the same lines, remembering, of course, that the forces will be much less, and in fact 0.46 of the lunar forces, owing to the ratio of distances and masses.

Results of considering variations of the sun's and moon's distances alone

Summarizing the above simply, assuming an ideal non-rotating earth, with the plane of the equator coincident with that of the earth's and moon's orbits:

(a) The dominant and lunar tide would at any place near the equator culminate on a line passing through the moon and earth's centres on both sides of the earth owing to the differential forces, and high water would occur twice every 29.53 days, this being the synodic or phase cycle between successive new moons (Fig. II, 7).

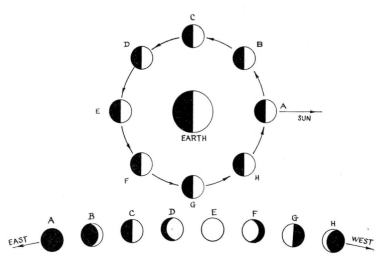

Fig. II, 7   Synodic cycle of moon's phases

(b) The dominant and lunar tide would also attain maximum high water values at positions on the earth's surface on the line of centres, at perigee (moon nearest to the earth) and a least high water value on the line of centres where the moon was at apogee (moon farthest from the earth) (Fig. II, 8).   The entire cycle from perigee to perigee known as the Anomalistic cycle, as stated above, occupies 27.50 days,

c

but the major axis of the moon's orbit will only come into line with the sun and moon's centres twice a year, once at apogee and once at perigee. Hence maxima and minima would occur annually, if we combine solar and lunar conjunctions.

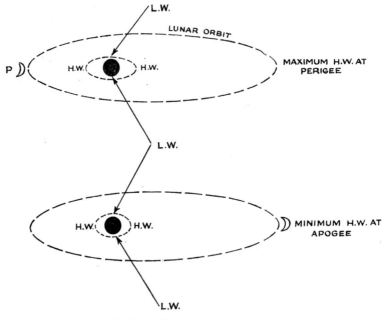

Fig. II, 8   Effects apogee and perigee

(c)   The sun's attraction being somewhat less than half that of the moon would have similar tractive effects on both sides of the earth.   These would be greatest on the line of centres at perihelion and least at aphelion, the entire solar tidal cycle occupying a solar year.

(d)   The tidal ellipsoid produced by the tractive forces of the sun and moon combined would be a resultant of both components the lunar effect being dominant, the solar having the effect of attracting the axis of the ellipsoid somewhat out of the line joining the centres of earth and moon (Fig. II, 9).

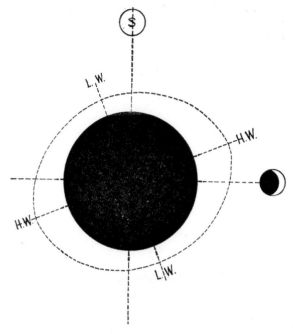

Fig. II, 9 Combined effect of lunar and solar tide.

Still assuming the orbits of the sun and moon to be in the plane of the equator on our ideal earth, the tidal result of the earth's rotation on its own axis in 24 hours must now be considered.

FUNDAMENTAL RESULTS OF EARTH'S ROTATION

On the equilibrium theory, the following diagram will show that a place on the equator would, disregarding friction, pass through a water envelope, assumed to be continuously adjusted to fixed astronomical forces, in such a manner that the water level experienced would alternate between high and low every 6 hours.

In Fig. II, 10, which is in plane of equator, T represents a tide gauge with zero at the earth's solid surface. The dotted line delineates the water envelope resulting from gravitational forces, disregarding friction, and assuming instant adjustment of the water mass to these forces, Subordinate figures indicate hours from noon.

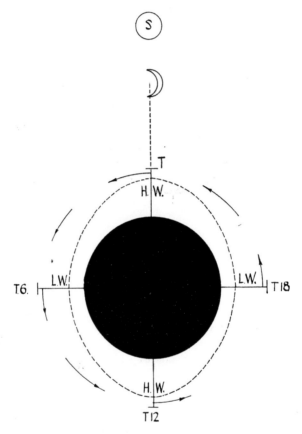

Fig. II, 10   Effect of earth's rotation on equilibrium envelope and imaginary recording on a tide gauge

As already shown, the equilibrium theory assumes an instant adjustment of the shape of the water envelope to the tractive forces which, of course, does not occur in nature. The tide gauge T in the diagram does not, of course, rotate in any sense through the water mass but rather through the *form* of the water envelope, which is assumed to be constantly related in shape and major axis to the fundamental astronomical forces.

On this assumption, the water surface would rise to a high-water level at T, would fall to low water as the gauge rotated to T_6, rise again to a high water level at T_{12}, fall again to low water at T_{18} and finally rise to highwater on recovering the position T.

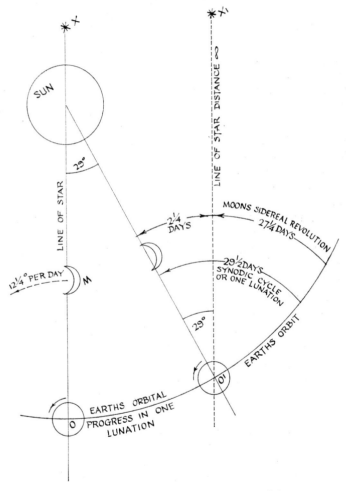

Fig. II, II   Time difference in moon's successive transits

Fundamental results of combining the moon's synodic revolution in her orbit, and the earth's annual revolution in its orbit around the sun

If the sun and moon remained in conjunction or *syzygies* as shown in the previous diagram, spring high waters would occur continuously at noon and midnight alternately at intervals of exactly 12 hours.

In fact the moon revolves around the earth (in the same direction as its rotation), and completes its synodic cycle from new moon to new moon through first, second, and third quarters in 29.53 days. The transit of the moon across the meridian averages 50 minutes later each day, Fig. II, 11.

At new moon and full moon (see Fig. II, 12) when the centres of sun, moon, and earth are in line, the maximum tidal attraction will be felt on the water envelope of the ideal earth and spring or extreme high-water will be experienced simultaneously on both sides of the earth, on the line of centres as previously shown. When however, the moon has moved some distance away from the sun, the resultant equilibrium crest will occur at a position intermediate between sun and moon, but, of course, nearer to the latter.

When after $7\frac{1}{2}$ days the moon has moved 90° away from the sun the tractive forces of the sun and moon will be acting in opposition and minimum or neap tidal effects will occur, the oscillation about mean sea level being much smaller than at springs, the high waters being lower and the low waters higher. Fig. II, 12 illustrates this.

Under these conditions spring and neap tides would occur at intervals of about $7\frac{1}{2}$ days and alternate high and low waters follow each other at intervals of 6 hours and 12 minutes.

The effect of intermediate positions of the moon between Conjunction (or Opposition) and Quadrature is shown in Fig. II, 13. In this diagram the resultant equilibrium "form" crest, or apex, is for the sake of illustration shown at a much greater angular distance from the moon than in fact. It will be observed that as the moon moves into the first quarter as shown in the centre diagram, the tidal crest forms behind the moon. Consequently the tide gauge site T passes the crest before the moon is on the meridian and the high tide which at springs occurred

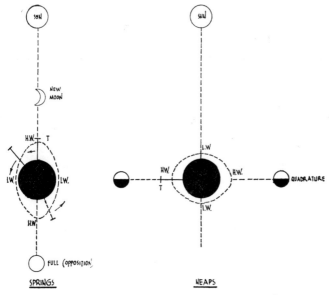

Fig. II, 12   Astronomical forces producing neap tides

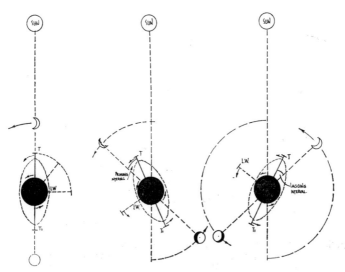

Fig. II, 13   Priming and lagging of equilibrium crest in marked semi-diurnal tide

at the moon's transit now occurs *before* the transit and is said to "prime."

The same phenomenon will occur in the third quarter when the moon is moving away from opposition to the sun and the second period of springs in the lunar cycle.

During the second and fourth quarters, however, the axis of the water envelope will be so disposed as to bring the tidal crest to the left or ahead of the position under the moon and local high water will occur *after* the moon's local transit and be said to "lag."

In Fig. II, 14 the details of the two high waters following new moon are shown.

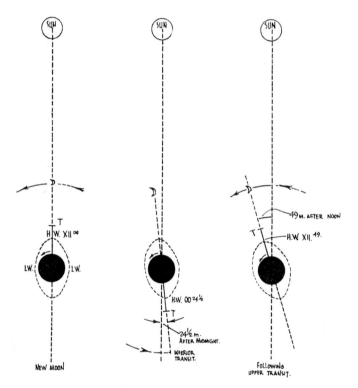

Fig. II, 14 Semi-diurnal high waters at tide gauge "T" at new moon, inferior transit, and following day, assuming H.W. crest under the moon, equator in plane of earth's and moon's orbits and constant angular rate of moon in orbit at 12.2° per day

In all these cases we have been considering the plane of the earth's rotation and those of the earth and moon's orbits to be coincident and the resultant tidal crest to be generated instantly by the astronomical tidal crest to be generated instantly by the astronomical forces. The result has been a system of semi-diurnal and alternating high and low waters varying with the moon's synodic cycle of phases known as a lunation, and modified by the varying distances of the sun and moon in their orbits.

In fact, the result of the astronomical forces and positions is not actually felt until a period of one or more days has elapsed. This lag is called the Age of the Tide and varies from $1\frac{1}{2}$ days in the North Atlantic Ocean (where semi-diurnal tides, as described, are dominant) to several days elsewhere. (Not to be confused with the age of waves).

We must now abandon our preliminary assumption of coincident planes of orbit and equator and consider the effects of the varying declinations of sun and moon, which in many localities are so dominant as to produce *diurnal* tides, where there is only one single high and one single low water every $24\frac{3}{4}$ hours.

The Effect of Declination upon the equilibrium tide

As the equator is set $23\frac{1}{2}°$ to the ecliptic (i.e. orbit of the earth around the sun), and the moon's orbit is set about $5° 9'$ to that of the earth, the earth's movement around the sun in conjunction with the revolution of the nodes of the moon's orbit through $360°$, in 18.6 years, will vary the moon's declination (or latitude where she is overhead on the meridian) up to a maximum of $28\frac{1}{2}°$ north and south which will recur at this interval (see Fig. II, 1).

As the moon's movement in latitude or declination has thus a possible range of $57°$ and her tractive influence is more than twice that of the sun, it would be surprising if large aberrations from semi-diurnal tidal phenomena giving two daily high waters did not occur from this cause. To illustrate this effect assuming the Equilibrium Theory, let us for the moment disregard the sun and concentrate on the moon's declinational effect.

In Fig. II, 15, let EQ represent the plane of the equator, let T and T^1, represent the position of a tide gauge rotating on the parallel XY. The tidal envelope is, of course, shown greatly exaggerated beyond equilibrium values for the purpose of illustration.

At the moon's transit T will experience the high water value of HY; 12½ hours later at the moon's inferior transit at T¹ the small high water value of GX will be experienced. At T again

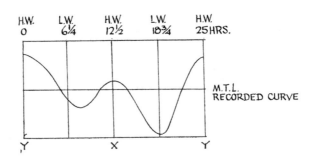

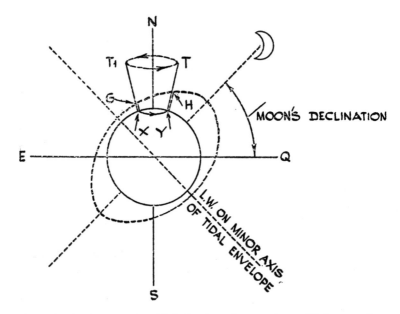

Fig. II, 15   Predominant diurnal declination effect on the equilibrium envelope

high water will be experienced 24¾ hours after the original superior or upper transit. This situation will in nature generally produce alternating higher and lower high waters daily. This inequality in height is called "Diurnal Inequality" (Fig. II, 16).

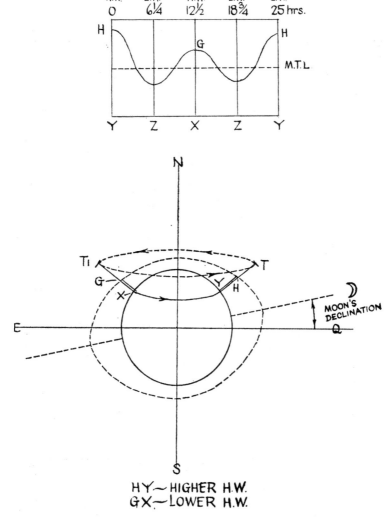

HY—HIGHER H.W.
GX—LOWER H.W.

Fig. II, 16 Lesser effect of small declination causing diurnal inequality

Whilst the equilibrium tide must on the equilibrium theory always manifest itself, except at the poles, under actual conditions in some localities it vanishes entirely for dynamical reasons peculiar to the site.

When the sun and moon are acting nearly in conjunction with, or opposition to, each other and the moon is in high declination the diurnal effect will clearly be marked when the sun attains its maximum declination of $23\frac{1}{2}°$ at the summer and winter solstices and is overhead in the tropics of Cancer and Capricorn respectively.

The greatest combined declination effect will occur when the moon's maximum declination of $28\frac{1}{2}°$ coincides with one or other of the solstices. As previously stated, the moon's maximum declination occurs every 18.6 years.

We see therefore, that the tidal effects of declination can produce diurnal inequality in heights under ordinary circumstances but that when the moon's declination is high, in many localities the smaller high water is effaced altogether from dynamical causes producing a diurnal or single daily high and low water (see Figs. II, 15 and 16).

Fig. II, 17 (A) shows the usual synodic or semi-diurnal tidal phenomena, giving two daily high waters with which we are

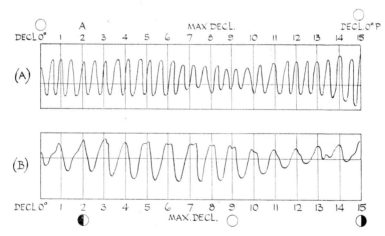

Fig. II, 17 Small scale curves Dover and Victoria, B.C., illustrating synodic (semi-diurnal) and diurnal (declination) tides (from Tides and Tidal Streams Warburg)
A = Apogee   B = Perigee

familiar on the shores of the North Atlantic; (B) illustrates diurnal tides with varying effects resulting from changes in the declination of moon and sun.

The period of the moon's declinational cycle, that is to say, from extreme north through south to extreme north, occupies what is known as a tropical month of 27.2 days. Where the tide is of a synodic or semi-diurnal character, diurnal inequality attains a maximum at extreme north or south declination of the moon and disappears when she is over the equator at zero declination.

In considering the combined declinational effect of the sun and moon it will be clear that if their resultant tractive forces are in the place of the equator, no daily inequality in high water heights will occur. Assuming that roughly $11°$ of the moon's declination is equivalent to $23\frac{1}{2}°$ of the sun's declination, in this respect, if the sun and moon *acting in conjunction* have declinations of $23\frac{1}{2}°$ north and $11°$ south respectively, no diurnal inequality should result as the plane of the extreme periphery of the water envelope would be in the plane of the equator.

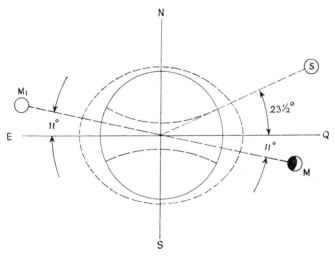

Fig. II, 18 Declinational balance of tractive forces

Also if the sun and moon were in opposition with declinations of $23\frac{1}{2}°$ north and $11°$ north respectively, no diurnal disturbance should result (see Fig. II, 18) for the same reason.

Inequality in time intervals between high waters from declinational causes

In addition to height inequality resulting from extreme declinations it must also be noted that there is also an inequality in the times elapsing between high to low waters and between low water to next high water.

An undisturbed semi-diurnal tide would, apart from priming and lagging due to the sun's influence, give successive high waters at regular intervals of 12 hours 25 minutes.

In actual fact the diurnal inequality from declinational causes is almost always accompanied by great irregularity in these intervals. In the Strait of Georgia, for example, this inequality may become as great as 8½ and 16¼ hours alternately.

Inequality of true intervals between new and full moon in the synodic or phase cycle

The period elapsing between successive new moons is 29.53 days. It does not follow, however, that full moons occur exactly half way through this cycle (or 14.76 days after new moon), as the angular motion of the moon in her orbit is not uniform but conforms to the laws of elliptical motion and is faster near perigee than at apogee.

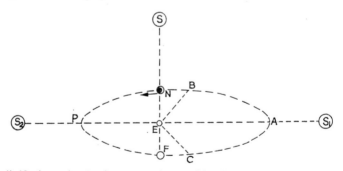

Fig. II, 19   Inequality in phase intervals caused by the moon's orbital movement

Kepler's law requires equal areas to be traversed or swept in equal times by a radial line joining the centres of moon and earth (see Fig. II, 19).

If area EBPCE = area BECAB the time of travel from the point B through P to C is equal to that taken to traverse the path from C through A to B. The points B and C are thus midway in time between perigee and apogee, and the speed of travel near perigee greater than that at apogee.

As the earth moves in its annual orbit round the sun the axis of the moon's orbit (itself changing relatively slowly) will move from coincidence with the line of centres joining sun and earth at apogee or perigee through various intermediate positions. If the sun's position is at S_1 or S_2 as in Fig. II, 19, then new and full moon will occur alternately at intervals of exactly half a lunar month and the succeeding new moon will recur at the same intervals after full, as the distance PNBA = ACFP.

If, on the other hand the line of centres between earth and sun is at right angles to the orbital axis PA, that is when the sun is at S, the new moon will occur at the position N, the full moon at F, the new moon recurring at N.

As the elliptical distances BAC and CPB are traversed in equal times the time interval between new and full traversed along the line NBACF is necessarily greater than that required to move along the line FPN from full to new. Hence when this situation occurs, as it does twice during the solar year, the actual intervals of time between new and full or full and new moon may be 13.94 days and 15.59 days respectively. It will thus be seen how very unequal it is possible for them to become.

The results of the above phenomena can be summarized as follows:

(a) New and full moons can occur at apogee or perigee or at intermediate positions of the anomalistic cycle or perigee interval.

(b) If the new moon is at perigee the succeeding full moon will be nearly at apogee, and vice versa.

(c) If one of the quarters occurs at apogee the next quarter will occur at perigee.

(d) In case (b) time intervals between spring tides at full or new moon are almost exactly half a lunar month.

(e) In case (c) the intervals between spring tides are unequal, and may differ by over $1\frac{1}{2}$ days.

Another feature of interest in these variations depends upon the curious astronomical fact that perigee does not fall back evenly around the synodic or lunar month, but "hangs" or remains close to new moon for three or four months. It then shifts rapidly through the quarters again "steadying up" and "hanging" as it were at the full moon before going on past the next quarter.

The resulting "perigee springs" giving maximum lunar effects at syzygies (conjunction or opposition of sun and moon) consequently recur for about three months in succession during the year before they fall off in height.

As a matter of interest, maximum perigee springs occur with sun in perihelion approximately every 1,600 years, with the axis of the moon and earth's orbits in coincidence with the line of nodes, that is with both sun and moon at zero declination. These phenomenal conditions give rise to the greatest possible astronomical tide-raising forces.

Such astronomical dispositions for maximum tractive forces have been calculated to occur at 3500 B.C., 1900 B.C., 250 B.C., A.D. 1433, A.D.3300.

Pettersson has credited them with climatic effects, inundations and ice formation, and has even connected them with the occurrence of earthquakes in areas of relative earth instability. He has also contended that from this cause Iceland was free of earthquakes from A.D. 800-1250 but that their frequency increased to a maximum from A.D. 1291-1348.

These theories have not been generally confirmed by scientists but are here recorded as of general interest.

Recapitulation

The results of our study of equilibrium effects in relation to astronomical cycles may be summed up in the tabulated form shown on page 54.

In concluding this section it is emphasised that we have been considering the equilibrium tide conceived as occurring without friction in a continuously adjusted deep-water envelope covering an ideal spheroid.

On the equator the maximum tidal range (or vertical difference in level between high and low water) with the sun and moon at their average distances from the earth is computed from gravitational formulae to be about 2.5 feet.

The extreme tidal range generated by the sun and moon at their closest distances and acting together is about 3 feet for the equilibrium tide, but in actual tides the ranges may vary considerably.

Qualitatively, however, it can be asserted with confidence that the following applications are true of the equilibrium tide:

(a) It is comprised of constant terms, diurnal oscillations and semi-diurnal oscillations.

(b) The diurnal tide is nil at zero declination and increases with declination.

(c) The tide varies mostly with the lunar distance and approximately as the cube of the parallax, or inversely as the cube of the distance.

The statement of the *Admiralty Manual of the Tides* (p. 32, art. 42), may fitly be quoted in concluding this section:

"The characteristic variations of the equilibrium tide exhibit the characteristic variations of the existing tide in greater or less degree."

Harmonic Analysis of tidal behaviour

Hitherto we have related the gravitational interactions of sun and moon and earth respectively to their cyclic movements in a general sense, but without attempting a synthesis. The method of harmonic analysis—founded mainly on the investigations of Laplace, suggested by Lord Kelvin and developed by Sir George Darwin—seeks to relate all cyclic tide-raising factors to their astronomical causes on the following assumptions:

(a) The complete tidal curve of heights at any place comprises the summation of a number of simple and quasi-independent oscillations of varying periods each corresponding to the tractive cycle of an astronomical disturbing force.

(b) The curve describing each constituent "wave" is the result of uniform harmonic motion and may be described as an oscillation about Mean Tide Level wherein the complete wave cycle, and that of its astronomical cause, have the same period.

(c) The vertical ordinates of each component curve above Mean Tide Level are in cosine relationship to the angular

D

movements of a point rotating about Mean Tide Level at amplitude radius, the angles of rotation being measured from a point at the vertex of the curve with radius normal to the plotted Mean Tide Level.

The entire radial revolution of 360° is coincident with the complete time-cycle of the relevant astronomical disturbing force. Thus in Fig. II, 20, if the vertical point of maximum elevation is regarded as zero, r = the amplitude of the constituent "wave" and θ the angular rotation from zero at vertex, then the ordinate of the curve at any time will be $r \cos \theta$ which is the elevation above or below M.T.L. according to sign.

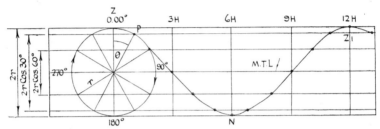

P = Point rotating uniformly about ⊙12 in hr cycle at radius
r = Amplitude
ZNZI = Curve of ordinates against time, describing resulting wave action

Fig. II, 20 Harmonic motion and resulting cosine curve

(d) The hourly angular speed of rotation is found by dividing 360° by the relevant astronomical cycle. For example the recurrence of high waters due to the lunar tidal cycle or interval between upper and lower transits is 12.42 hours. The hourly angular rate of rotation would, therefore, be:

$$\frac{360}{12.42} = 28°.98$$

The quantity is known as the speed number n.

(e) When the true relationships and phase lags of the various constituent waves have, after continuous observations, been related to their astronomical causes by close analysis, tidal prediction may be made from the calculated relative positions of sun, moon, and earth, by combining the various harmonic "waves" and obtaining a resultant curve.

(f) The "radius" of each constituent is equal to the amplitude
for which the particular disturbing force is responsible,
Fig. II, 21.

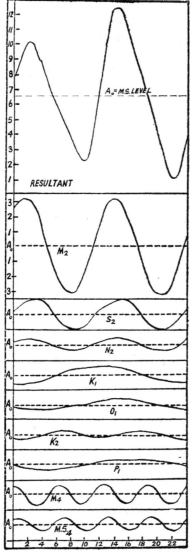

Fig. II, 21 Curve predicted from nine harmonic constituents
(from Introduction to Oceanography—Johnstone)

51

(g) The tidal constituents are denoted by letter symbols which are abbreviations of their main characteristic, the subscript numbers indicating whether they are diurnal, semi-diurnal, quarter diurnal, sixth diurnal, etc.

   (i) The main and lunar semi-diurnal constituent is accordingly M_2 and has a speed number of 28° .98 (as above in (d).)

   (ii) The solar semi-diurnal constituent is S_2 with a speed number of 30°.

   (iii) The following constituents are shown tabulated, those bracketed being compound as described in (f) above.

Symbol of Constituent	Speed Number	Description and function
N_2 L_2	28°.440 29°.528	Describing semi-diurnal variation caused by the monthly variations in the moon's distance.
K_2	30°.082	Soli-lunar constituent describing variables due to changes in declination of sun and moon throughout their orbital cycles.
K_1 O_1	15°.041 13°.943	Describing the diurnal oscillation due to the moon's declination. They balance each other when this is zero. K_1 also has the same speed number as the constituent due to the sun's declinational cycle and is thus—as in the case of K_2—solilunar with a dual function.
P_1	14°.959	Complementary constituent to K_2 in its solar function.
Mf	1°.098	Moon's fortnightly constituent.

Symbol of Constituent	Speed Number	Description and function
Mm	0°.544	Moon's monthly constituent.
Sa	0°.041	Sun's *annual* distance (parallax) constituent, perigee to perigee.
S sa	0°.082	Sun's *semi-diurnal*, declinational constituent—vernal to autumnal equinox.
M_4 ($=2M_2$)	57°.968 ⎱	Quarter diurnal distortion of progressive wave.
MS_4 ($=M_2+S_2$)	58°.984 ⎰	

The above are some of the main constituents into which the tidal curve may be analysed, but there are, of course, higher species, e.g. sixth, eighth, and tenth diurnal as well as long term constituents, the latter describing the effects of the longer astronomical cycles.

Mechanical predicting devices

Clearly the above method of analysis lends itself readily to mechanical methods. If we know the amplitude values, phase lags and speed numbers of the constituents involved we can arrange a series of moving cranks with corresponding radii rotating in the same vertical plane at the respective speeds of the constituents they represent: the algebraic sum of the elevation of the ends of the cranks above the horizontal plane containing their centres, at any instant, will represent the value of sea level above mean sea level at any instant as in Fig. II, 22.

Horizontally slotted link devices can be employed to communicate the vertical movement of each to a series of pulleys, and it is simple to arrange a summation wire passing around the pulleys etc., secured at one end but with the movable end arranged to actuate a pen in contact with a continuous recording device which will plot the algebraic sum of all their vertical components ($H \cos \theta$) against time as shown in Fig. II, 22.

SUMMARY OF ASTRONOMICAL TIDAL FACTORS (*vide* pp. 52, 53).

Tidal Effects	Related Astronomical cycle	Period	Cause
Twice daily or semi-diurnal	Interval between moon's upper and lower transits. Dominantly lunar.	12.4 hours	Rotation of the earth and resultant of sun and moon's tractive forces causing high water on both sides of the earth.
Once daily or diurnal	Interval between succeeding upper or lower transits of sun and/or moon.	24.8 hours (moon)	Declination of sun and/or moon and rotation of the earth.
Fortnightly interval between Spring Tides	Half revolution of moon's orbit	14-76 days (Mean)	Conjunction with sun to opposition. Opposition to conjunction (or simply interval between syzygies).
Fortnightly interval between maximum diurnal effects at upper and lower moon's transits alternately	Maximum south to maximum north declination or vice versa	13.6 days	Varying declination and rotation of the earth. Apices of tidal ellipsoid maintained on line of centres on both sides of the ideal earth on varying latitudes.
Monthly	Anomalistic or perigee to perigee.	27.5 days	Variation of tractive forces due to changes in the moon's distance.
Half-yearly	Half revolution of earth in orbit giving cycle of sun's declination from zero through extreme north or south and back to zero.	182.62 days	Orbital movement of earth.
Yearly	Variation of sun's distance.	365.24 days	Movement of earth in elliptical orbit.
Long period. Lunar apsides cycle	Rotation of axis of moon's orbit.	8.8 years	Gravitational.
Nodal cycle	Revolution or regression of moon's nodes.	18.61 years	Soli-lunar cycle relating planes of orbits.
Metonic cycle	Metonic cycle of recurrence of lunar phases.	19 years	Soli-lunar cycle relating synodic period.
Saros cycle	Saros cycle, or recurrence of eclipses, that is, coincidence of line of centres of earth, sun, and moon.	18.03 years	Soli-lunar cycle.
Perigee/Perihelion Syzygy cycle	Recurrence of positions with earth in perihelion and moon in perigee at syzygies. (Conjunction or opposition).	1,600 years	Orbital cycles, harmonizing synodic anomalistic and nodal cycles.

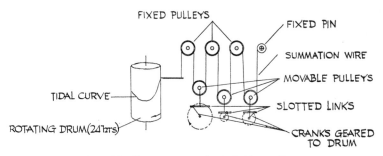

Fig. II, 22 Elementary mechanical tide predictor

ELECTRONIC PREDICTING DEVICES

Quite obviously any mechanical computing device, such as we have described in the previous section, can now be superseded by electronic computers capable of achieving an accurate resultant curve from the several harmonic constituents without the inevitable increment of error due to mechanical features, slackness of wire, friction etc.

For some time the economics of electronic prediction did not call for any major abandonment of the many excellent mechanical devices in international use giving results satisfactory for all navigational and operational purposes.

Research and development in the electronic field have now, however, reached the stage where accurate and rapid prediction can be achieved at economic cost and whilst the mechanical devices will be retained in many places during the foreseeable future, scientific analysis and prediction by the newer principles must increasingly come into use.

BIBLIOGRAPHY

MARMER—The Tide.
DARWIN—The Tide.
DAWSON, D. N. S.—Tides and Tidal Streams. Canada (1920).
MURRAY, M. T.—Tidal Analysis with an Electronic Digital Computer (Liverpool Tidal Institute, 1963). Also 1964 Annual Report by L.T.I.

CHAPTER THREE

Tidal theory today

THE TIDES AS THEY EXIST

IT IS characteristic of the last century that tidal phenomena in the oceans, seas, and gulfs of our planet have come under a co-ordinated and universal scrutiny previously impossible. Observations had long proved that the rise and fall of tides at islands in the deep oceans conformed roughly to the small spring range of 2-3 feet, deduced from the equilibrium theory.

In Fig. III, 1 we see three simultaneous tidal curves continuously recorded at Avonmouth, Gibraltar and Heligoland. All are semi-diurnal.

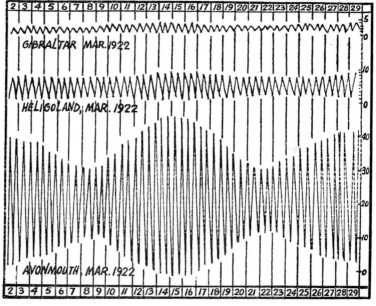

Fig. III, I   Three characteristic curves on small scale, Gibraltar, Avonmouth and Heligoland (from Introduction to Oceanography—Johnstone)

56

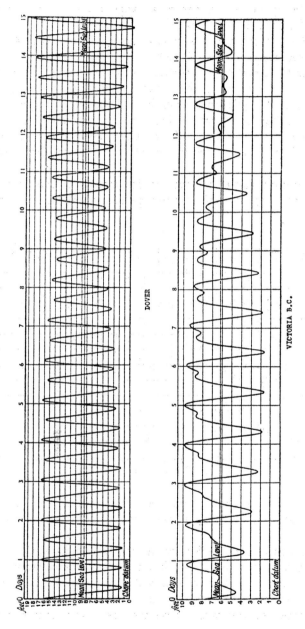

Fig. III, 2   Curves at Dover and Victoria B.C. (from Tides and Tidal Streams—Warburg)

The Gibraltar record shows a range agreeing with values observed in the deep oceans.

The Avonmouth curve records a spring range of over 40 feet and a neap range of over 20 feet.

All three records show that these tides are synodic in type and conform to the times of the lunar phases, springs and neaps, occurring about 1½ days after syzygies and quadrature respectively.

Again in Fig. III, 2 we see harmonically predicted curves for Dover and Victoria B.C. which agree very closely with observed values. The Dover curve is almost entirely semi-diurnal and synodic.

The Victoria curve, however, is dominantly diurnal, the low waters occurring for only a short period, approximately every 24.7 hours.

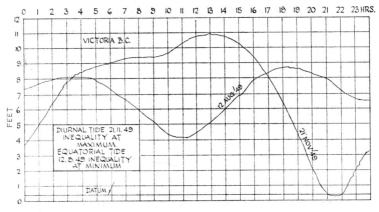

Fig. III, 3 Typical diurnal tide, Victoria, B.C. on large scale (from U.S. Coast and Geodetic Survey)

The moon's declination increases from zero on the first day to maximum on the 8th day returning to zero on or near the 15th day.

The moon's diurnal effect consequently dominates more and more from the 2nd to the 9th day, decreasing thereafter and the result is seen in a double high water phenomenon, the peaks being separated by about 9 hours.

The other features of the curve are due to solar influence also of a diurnal nature as well as semi-diurnal. The tide at this station is clearly of the "mixed" variety being composed of the diurnal and semi-diurnal tides, the latter predominating only when the sun and moon are on the equator.

On the other hand there are tides which are almost completely diurnal in character. These are generally of small range which is at maximum value at the times of the moon's maximum declination in accordance with the equilibrium theory. Such tides are sometimes called "tropic" tides. A tidal curve for Victoria B.C. (Fig. III, 3) shows high waters culminating approximately every 24¾ hours at levels of about 11 feet above L.W. Datum Typical diurnal curves for Northumberland Strait, Challeur Bay, and Strait of Georgia are also shown in Fig. III, 4.

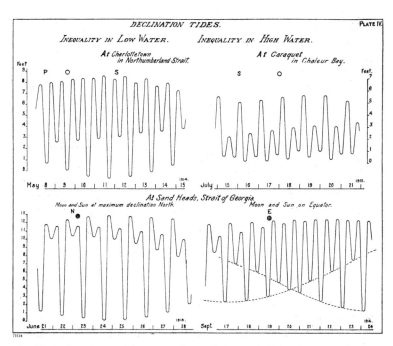

Fig. III, 4 Canadian tidal curves (from Tides and Tidal Streams—Dawson)
N = Moon at extreme North declination
S = Moon at extreme South declination
E = Moon on Equator. Moon shaded is new at change, unshaded at full
P = Moon at perigee

At Victoria B.C. the range of the diurnal tide may exceed 9 feet and at Kua Kam, French Indo-China, it may be greater than 12 feet but the range of such tides is generally small.

The Pacific Ocean and its boundaries appear to be favourable to the occurrence of small-range diurnal tides although these also occur on the Atlantic coasts, where hydraulic conditions are made suitable by the boundaries of gulfs and straits.

It is important also to remember that the solar constituent S_2 sometimes exceeds the lunar M_2 in the Pacific area, probably due to the resonance of the *solar* disturbing period with the natural period of the body of water affected.

In consequence, under these circumstances the diurnal tide due to solar influence dominates that due to the moon.

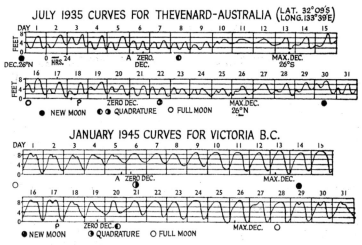

Fig. III, 5 (Top) Thevenard curve—Australia, showing constant afternoon H.W. due to dominant solar (S_2) and diurnal (K^1) constituents with sun in south declination. (Bottom) Victoria, B.C., curves showing typical diurnal (declinational) tide

In such a case (see Fig. III, 5) maximum range will occur near the times when the sun is in the tropics of Cancer and Capricorn with the lunar forces at maxima assisting near that time.

It is thus possible for the diurnal tide to "hang" near a solar hour for the entire lunar month where the solar constituent S_2 is greater than the lunar M_2 and the diurnal characteristics or constituents are dominant as in the case of Thevenard (Australia) Fig. III, 5.

Recapitulating, a primary grouping of world tides is made as follows:

(a) *Semi-diurnal* varying in range with the moon's phases.

(b) *Diurnal* varying with declination, especially that of the moon.

(c) *Mixed*, diurnal and semi-diurnal, these characteristics varying with the moon's declination and phases and also with solar forces when these are dominant.

The semi-diurnal tides predominate on the North Atlantic seaboards with some exceptions on the eastern coasts of North America, notably on the north shore of Prince Edward Island in the Gulf of St. Lawrence and the northern half of the Gulf of Mexico.

Semi-diurnal tides give the largest ranges in the world which occur off the British Isles—notably the Bristol Channel, where the spring range at Avonmouth is nearly 50 feet—in the Bay of Fundy where they may reach a maximum height of over 50 feet and on the French Coast (see p. 177).

The strictly diurnal tide is rare, but occurs notably in parts of the Pacific Ocean and is almost pure at Do San (Kua Kam) in French Indo-China and the northern half of the Gulf of Mexico.

The mixed type prevails on part of the Australian coast, on the Pacific coast of North America, on the eastern shores of Asia and adjacent islands.

A series of successive high and low waters is here given for the port of Seattle, U.S.A. for 19-22 October 1932, with the moon's declination at 28°N. to illustrate diurnal declinational effect.

	H.W.	L.W.
19th	10.7	0.1
	9.3	7.8
20th	10.6	0.4
	8.9	8.1
21st	10.7	0.7
	8.3	8.1
22nd	10.9	1.1
	7.8	7.6

The behaviour of such tides is obviously of critical importance for the access of deep draught ships to the ports at which they occur and it is obvious that the function of the moon's declination should be carefully watched by navigators for rough predictions in the absence of more precise forecasts.

Dr. W. Bell Dawson who superintended the tidal survey of Canada contended that his area contained all the leading varieties of tide and that a more accurate and apt description of the three outstanding types would be as follows:

    (i) The Synodic or Phase type of semi-diurnal tide varying in range fortnightly from springs to neaps and covering 57.06 tide intervals.

    (ii) The Declinational or diurnal type of tide, varying in range monthly from minimum declination through maximum and covering 52.79 tide intervals.

    (iii) The Anomalistic or perigee/apogee tide varying dominantly with the moon's distance over the anomalistic month and covering 53.24 tide intervals.

None of these types are ever entirely pure, but one of the three features is nearly always dominant. Thus the British tides would be Synodic and the diurnal and mixed tides dominantly Declinational as in the case of Do Son and Seattle respectively, also Victoria B.C. Fig. III, 5.

The Anomalistic or perigee tide was not considered in the former classification under (a), (b) and (c) but it is well known that in some localities the variation in range between the moon's perigee and apogee is greater than that manifest between springs and neaps.

The outstanding example of this is seen in the Bay of Fundy and Hudson's Strait where the variation in range between apogee and perigee dominates to the exclusion of phase or declinational cycles (see Fig. III, 6). The following table also illustrates this feature.

Whilst the phenomenon of double high or low water peaks often occurs in all the leading types of tide, it is of interest to note the semi-diurnal double high water peaks which occur notably in the English Channel at Southampton, Havre, and Honfleur (Fig. III, 7) and off the Dutch coast (Fig. III, 8). See also Appendix V.

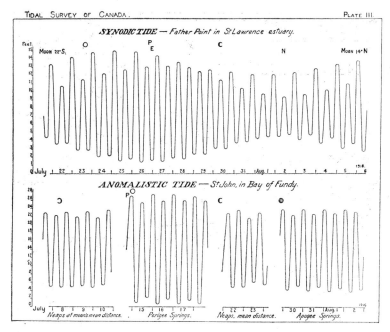

Fig. III, 6 Bay of Fundy curves (from Tides and Tidal Streams—Dawson)

Comparison of Tidal Rise between Burntcoat Head and St. Johns, New Brunswick in the Bay of Fundy. See Fig. III, 6a

Description of Tide	St. Johns N.B.		*Burntcoat Head	
	Range in Feet	Diff.	Range in Feet	Diff.
At Perigee Range at Springs	26.60 ⎤		50.50 ⎤	
At apogee, Range at Springs	19.92 ⎦	6.68	40.18 ⎦	10.32
Mean Spring range	23.26 ⎤		45.34 ⎤	
At moon's mean distance. Range	18.04 ⎦	5.22	38.78 ⎦	6.56
Average range during month	20.65		42.06	

* N.B.   Burntcoat Head outside E. margin of Fig. III, 6a

Fig. III, 6a Chart of the Bay of Fundy (natural scale reduced)

In addition the inversion of this feature in the semi-diurnal double low water peaks at Portland is a remarkable phenomenon (Fig. III, 9) known as the Gulder.

In the above general description our remarks have been confined purely to the vertical movement, or ranges, of the tides described, but it is necessary also to remember that the regularity of the occurrence of high and low water varies considerably, especially in the case of the diurnal and mixed tides, and also that the intervals between the action of the maximum astronomical tractive forces and the corresponding maximum tidal effect manifested at different localities (known as the Age of the Tide) is by no means constant.

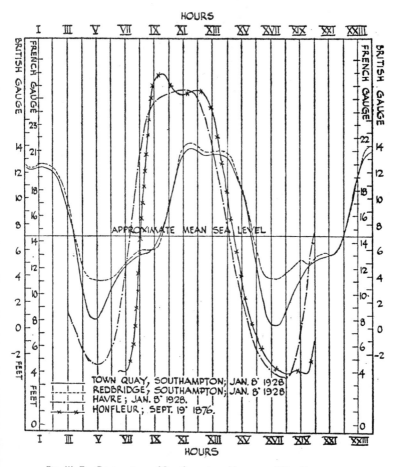

Fig. III, 7   Comparison of Southampton, Havre, and Honfleur curves

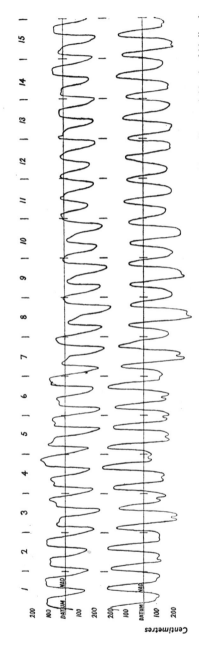

Fig. III, 8 Curves recorded on the Dutch Coast (from Mr. Van de Wetering) (Top) Den Helden. (Bottom) Hook of Holland

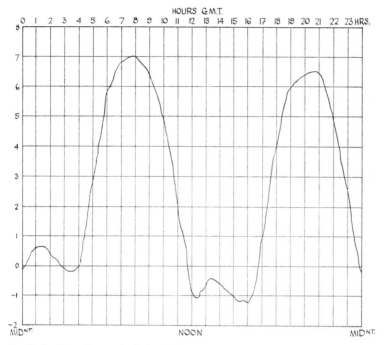

HOURS G.M.T.

Fig. III, 9 Typical record of the Gulder, Portland, showing double low waters

The age of the tide has an average value of $+1\frac{1}{2}$ days and this period is true for the semi-diurnal tides of the North Atlantic and the British Isles.   The age of the Tide varies in some localities up to $+7$ days, but at a few others is actually negative, that is the maximum tidal effect *precedes* the manifestation of the maximum astronomical tractive forces.

In the case of a semi-diurnal tide the lunitidal interval between the moon's transit at high water full or new moon varies little and is a useful constant, although in the case of diurnal-declinational or anomalistic tides of a mixed character it is useless and even misleading.

As previously observed, careful observation does not confirm that the tidal waves travel directly and simply from the Southern Ocean up the great oceanic tracts, channels, bays, and gulfs, but rather reveals the remarkable fact that the tidal waves often travel in contrary directions on their opposite shores with small areas

67

near their axes in which there is no vertical tidal movement whatsoever (see Fig. III, 10).

This phenomenon has led to the postulation of amphidromic or "no-tide" points (or areas) with co-tidal lines radiating therefrom with roughly concentric range "circles" increasing in range values as they recede from their roughly common centre.

Furthermore, observation shows that the movement of such co-tidal lines is, except in small deep seas like the Caspian, generally counter-clockwise in the Northern hemisphere and clockwise in the Southern. The somewhat similar rule for the movement of cyclonic wind systems would naturally suggest a common cause in the earth's rotation and this is confirmed by the theories of modern tidal mathematicians which we can now very cursorily examine.

Co-tidal maps illustrating possible features in the Atlantic and Pacific Oceans are shown in Figs. III, 10A, and 10B.

Before concluding this chapter it should be noted that observation of tidal behaviour in large gulfs and estuaries had for long suggested the notion of standing oscillations similar to the slip-slop movement artificially generated in a longitudinal tank filled with water.

When set in motion, high and low levels alternate at each end of the tank about a transverse axis or nodal line situated at the centre of its length. Along this nodal line there would be no *vertical* movement, but the necessary maximum horizontal oscillation in flow for the alternative supply at each end where levels attained maximum values (see Fig. III, 11).

In the English Channel this phenomenon has long been noted, high water at Dover occurring approximately at the time of low water at Devonport and vice versa.

Whilst there is no strictly nodal point an area of small range exists near the Isle of Wight (see Fig. III, 12) but the general result of observations is to indicate an approximation to a standing oscillation between Land's End and Dover. Modifications due to friction, the Cherbourg peninsula, the uneven bottom section, and the effect of the earth's rotation are also apparent.

Modern tidal theory applies the principles of stationary or standing oscillations to the larger oceanic areas with remarkable and illuminating results.

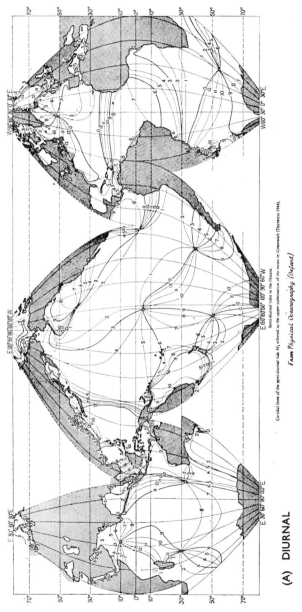

Co-tidal lines of the semi-diurnal tide M_2 referred to the upper culmination of the moon in Greenwich (DIETRICH 1944).
Semi-diurnal tide in the Oceans.

From *Physical Oceanography (Defant)*

Fig. III, 10A   Possible amphidromic systems of co-tidal lines in N. and S. Atlantic Oceans

(A) DIURNAL

69

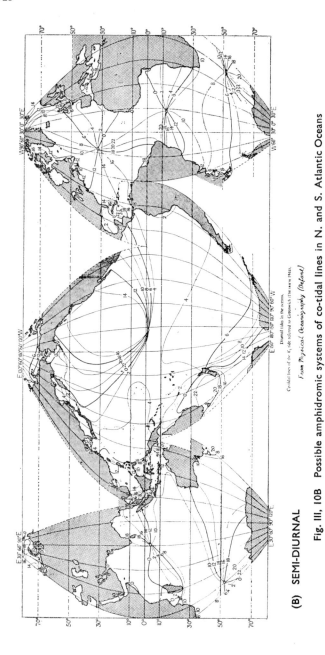

(B) SEMI-DIURNAL

Fig. III, I0B   Possible amphidromic systems of co-tidal lines in N. and S. Atlantic Oceans

From Physical Oceanography (Defant)

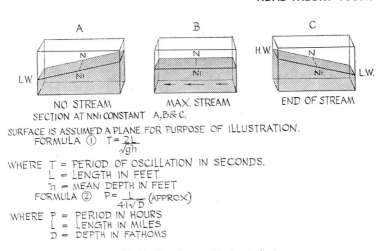

NO STREAM   MAX. STREAM   END OF STREAM
SECTION AT NNi CONSTANT A,B & C.
SURFACE IS ASSUMED A PLANE FOR PURPOSE OF ILLUSTRATION.

FORMULA ① $T = \dfrac{2L}{\sqrt{gh}}$

WHERE T = PERIOD OF OSCILLATION IN SECONDS.
    L = LENGTH IN FEET.
    h = MEAN DEPTH IN FEET

FORMULA ② $P = \dfrac{L}{4 \cdot 1 \sqrt{D}}$ (APPROX)

WHERE P = PERIOD IN HOURS
    L = LENGTH IN MILES
    D = DEPTH IN FATHOMS

Fig. III, 11   Standing oscillation in basin

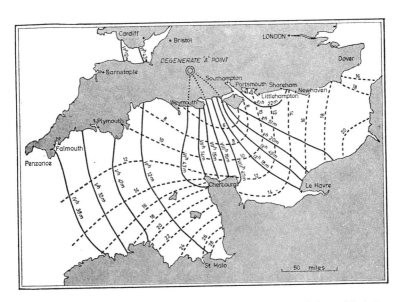

Fig. III, 12   Co-tidal lines of the English Channel (reproduced from Admiralty Chart 5058) Arabic figures give range of M2 tide. Roman numerals give time of local H.W. full and change

OUTLINE OF MODERN TIDAL THEORY

Tidal knowledge has not yet achieved such finality as to enable the tides to be explained fully and quantitatively without reference to observed values, but great strides are being made towards this ideal.

Three fundamental conceptions in tidal dynamics have provided the bases from which the investigation is successfully proceeding, namely:

(1) The theory of standing oscillations (see Fig. III, 11).
(2) The theory of resonance or synchronism between the natural oscillation periods of water masses in bays, gulfs, seas, and oceans and cyclic rhythms of the astronomical disturbing forces, the latter being of course, capable of precise prediction.
(3) The application of gyroscopic principles to determine the effect of the earth's rotation upon those masses of water which are necessarily set in motion horizontally by hydraulic factors, due to the differences in level of the sea surface induced by the tractive forces.

1. Standing Oscillations

Fig. III, 11, shows that when the standing wave is at rest at the moment of high and low water, it is stored with potential energy, which is converted into kinetic energy in adjusting the surface by maximum flow through the constant area of the cross section at N.N. Whilst variations of the disturbing force will produce proportionally greater or less amplitudes in the oscillation, the period of oscillation for a given quantity of fluid, contained in a tank or basin, is constant and neglecting friction, can be expressed in terms of the length of the receptacle as:

$$T = \frac{2l}{\sqrt{gh}}$$

Where T = period in seconds.

l = length in feet of tank, basin or gulf.

h = mean depth in feet.

g = 32.2.

Incidentally $\sqrt{gh}$ is the expression for the speed of a free progressive wave, and has valuable applications over a wide range of fluid mechanics.

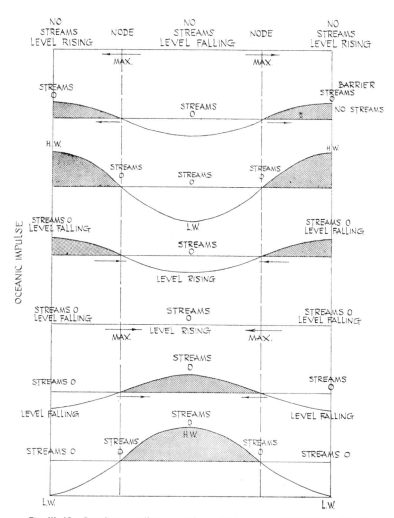

Fig. III, 13 Standing oscillation with multiple nodes (A.M.T.) modified

73

The simple example given can be elaborated into more complex phenomena where multiple nodes occur as shown in Fig. III, 13.

If a barrier is placed where shown, the system will not be disturbed as the stream velocity here is zero; also if we place barriers at a distance from the first barrier, and at points at intervals of half a wave-length where $v = 0$ under all circumstances, the system will remain undisturbed in profile.

Again, in theory, if a primary progressive wave of the same period and amplitude be introduced in phase on the left side of the diagram, the system would maintain oscillation in resonance with the primary wave.

The formula for the period of a multiple standing oscillation is:

$$T = \frac{2l}{\sqrt{gh}} - (1, 2, 3 \ldots .)$$

It will be noted that the placing of a barrier merely turns the progressive wave formation without alteration of profile into a *reflected* wave, and that points at which the system would be unaffected by barriers are located at intervals of *half* a wave-length. No horizontal streams occur at such points which in plan are actually nodal lines.

2. Resonance with astronomical tractive rhythms

Theory indicates the possibility of resonance between the oceanic tide and a standing oscillation in an arm of the sea with a length equal to half or quarter of the wave-length of a progressive wave appropriate to its depth (Fig. III, 14).

The length in this case of such a gulf or arm of the sea would be given by:

$$l = \tfrac{1}{2} T \sqrt{gh} \quad \text{or} \quad \tfrac{1}{4} T \sqrt{gh}$$

In the first case the oceanic high water at the entrance would coincide in time with the *low water* of equal amplitude at the head of the gulf; no water would flow into the latter which would receive only kinetic energy from the oceanic pulse.

If, for example, the gulf was 50 fathoms deep throughout, the length required for synchronism with a semi-diurnal oceanic pulse would be about 350 miles and for a diurnal pulse about 700 miles.

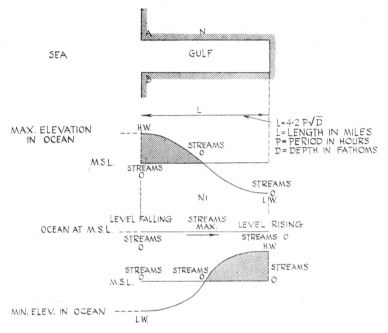

Fig. III, 14 Resonance of Standing Wave in gulf with oceanic pulse (A.M.T.)

In the case of the great oceans and seas the kinetic energy is generated by the astronomical tractive forces.

To quote the Admiralty Manual "the width of the Atlantic Ocean is quite large enough for resonance to occur within the ocean. A mean depth of 3 miles would only require a sea 3,000 miles long to give resonance with a period of 12 hours. It can, therefore, be seen that tides in the Atlantic Ocean are in all probability generated within the ocean and *owe little, if anything, to the tides in the southern ocean.*"

The actual oceans do not, of course, conform to the geometrically simple cases quoted. Also co-tidal lines joining points where high water times synchronize for any ocean are only, as yet, theoretically determined and the effect of friction must predominate near the continental shelves.

The relations between reflected and stationary waves are illustrated by Fig. III, 15 which shows a rectangular arm of the

75

sea *without friction* and which is assumed to have a section of
uniform area and a barrier at the head at Z. The length is one
wave-length of a standing oscillation maintained by an oceanic
pulse, with no streams at the entrance.

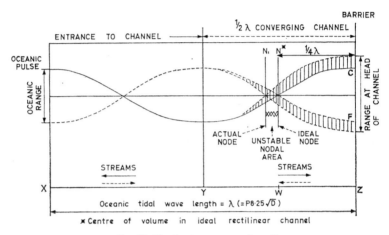

Fig. III, 15 Stationary wave in gulf

C = Speed of progressive waves 8.25 $\sqrt{D}$ (*knots*)
T = Period in hours
λ = Wave length in nautical miles
D = Depth in fathoms

If the length of the gulf is reduced to YZ there will be no
streams at the entrance Y and low and high waters will occur
simultaneously at Y and Z respectively with a node at N where
maximum streams occur. The length required for this system
would be half a wave-length and the ranges at the entrance and
head of the gulf would be equal if section was uniform.

If the entrance of the gulf is now moved to W, streams at N
will be at maximum rate at Mean Tide Level (M.T.L.) but no
change of level will in theory be experienced at the entrance.

Progressive wave-length: C × T

or   12C for semi-diurnal period.

= 100 $\sqrt{D}$ (Approx.)

or   24C for diurnal period = 200 $\sqrt{D}$ (approx.)

For semi-diurnal period.

Length in diagram $\lambda = 100 \sqrt{D}$ = length of semi-diurnal free wave

Length YZ in diagram $= \frac{1}{2}\lambda = 50 \sqrt{D} = \frac{1}{2}$ length of semi-diurnal free wave

Length of Gulf WZ in diagram $= 25 \sqrt{D} = \frac{1}{4}$ length of semi-diurnal free wave.

The water level will oscillate between the profiles NC and N F over the period of the oscillation and the length of such a system with major movement at the head of the gulf will be one quarter of a wave-length.

If L = wave-length of the oscillation (λ in diagram)

T = period in hours.

C = speed of the primary oceanic progressive oscillation *in knots* $(\sqrt{gh})$

D = depth in fathoms; we may summarize the theory as follows for a semi-diurnal pulse:

If we consider the $\frac{1}{4}L$ gulf as a converging one it will be found that the reduced width of section in the flood entry will cause an increase in HW level as indicated by shading.

On the ebb, levels will fall as shown and there will be a *small* range at the entrance and a virtual node at N_1.

In such a case the range will increase towards the head, high water occurring at nearly the same time throughout the gulf.

Whilst no completely satisfactory theory covering all the natural phenomena has been evolved, the above at least gives a rough pictorial idea of governing principles and has the merit of approximating very fairly to the values found in nature.

For example:

(a) In the English Channel the average depth approximates 36 fathoms giving free progressive $\lambda = L = 100 \sqrt{D} = 600$ miles.

Disregarding the complex natural factors, friction, converging margins etc., the channel roughly approximates 300 miles in length—assuming a barrier at Dover—and is, therefore dominated by an $\dfrac{L}{2}$ standing oscillation, high and low waters in fact occurring simultaneously off Cornwall and off Dover respectively.

(b) Long Island Sound, the eastern entrance to New York Harbour, has a length of about 80 miles and an average depth of 11 fathoms. Streams and range at the entrance are $3\frac{1}{2}$ knots and $2\frac{1}{2}$ feet respectively. At Execution Rocks near the western end of the Sound the mean range is $7\frac{1}{2}$ feet and streams are negligible. Over the entire length of the Sound the high waters occur almost simultaneously.

Again, using the depth as a criterion, the wave-length is given by $100\sqrt{D} = 100 \times 3.3 = 330$ miles. Clearly this oscillating system is of the stationary wave $\frac{L}{4}$ variety $\left(= \frac{330}{4} = 82.5 \text{ miles}\right)$ and the observed facts generally confirm this.

(c) The Bay of Fundy, famed for the greatest tidal range in the world at Burntcoat Head and Noel Bay, gives an excellent justification for the use of our approximate formula for responses to semi-diurnal tidal pulses.

The average depth of the Bay is 40 fathoms.

Therefore $L = 100\sqrt{D} = 100 \times 6.3 = 630$ miles.

Consequently $\frac{L}{4} = 158$ miles which agrees approximately with the measured length of 170 miles.

Decreasing width and shoaling side margins accentuate the range of this remarkable semi-diurnal standing oscillation and *the effect of the earth's gyration is to increase the ranges on the southern side of the Bay.*

The mean progressive ranges are as follows:

North Shore		South Shore	
	feet		feet
Nantucket Island	1.2	Cape Sable	9.0
Minomy Point	3.7	Yarmouth	14.0
Nanset Harbour	6.0	Grand Passage	18.2
Gloucester	8.9	Digby Gut	24.1
West Quoddy Head	15.7	Port George	27.8
St. John	20.9	Black Rock Light	31.5
Quaco	26.3	Horton Bluff	42.0
Folly Point	39.4	Noel Bay	44.2

High water occurs throughout much of the Bay almost simultaneously, and the degree of synchronism is so high that the monthly effect of the moon's distance on heights is, as previously stated, greater than the difference between springs and neaps.

To determine periods of these stationary wave systems given length in miles l and depth D, the following reciprocal formulae will give good approximations.

(a) For $\dfrac{L}{2}$ system with node at centre of length, $T = \dfrac{1}{4.1\ \sqrt{D}}$

(Fig. III, 15).

(b) For $\dfrac{L}{4}$ system with node near entrance, $T = \dfrac{1}{2.1\ \sqrt{D}}$

(Fig. III, 15 WZ).

As a guide to the theoretical relation of natural periods of 12 and 24 hours respectively to length and depth of rectangular and geometrically simple enclosed seas, the diagram shown in Fig. III, 16 has been calculated from the fundamental formula $l = \tfrac{1}{2}T\ \sqrt{gh}$, or in simpler if more approximate terms:

$$l = 4.1\ T\ \sqrt{D}$$

Where l = length in nautical miles.

  T = period of oscillation in hours.

  D = depth in fathoms.

On examining these curves it will be observed that when the depth increases above 1,000 fathoms the gradient of the curve of the semi-diurnal period is steeper and varies less with the length than with the depth.   Similarly in the case of the diurnal curve, at twice the length of sea indicated by the semi-diurnal curve, the effect of length diminishes appreciably.

This would seem to indicate that the wider oceans, e.g., the Pacific, are more liable to respond to the diurnal forces, although in fact no adequate or precise theory has yet been devised to cover such cases.

It does appear, however, that in a wide ocean like the Pacific, with a north-south extent of about 130° and an east west extent of over 180°, the diurnal and declinational rhythms of the tractive forces induce resonant wave motion of the diurnal character

79

generally observed in this area. The results of a careful mathematical treatment of a hypothetical ocean with meridians 180° apart and a depth of 14,520 feet by Professor Proudman and Dr. Doodson give some indication that this is the case.

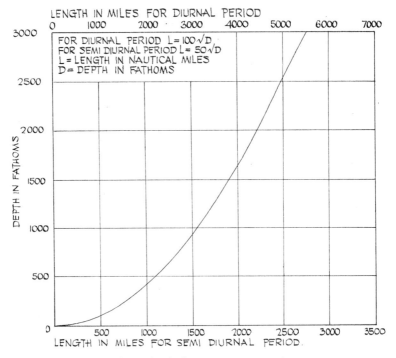

Fig. III, 16 Diagram relating depth of oceans or seas to stationary wave resonance for diurnal and semi-diurnal astronomical tractive cycles

3. Gyroscopic effect on systems of standing oscillations. Coriolis Force

The transmission of energy from the periodic rhythms of astronomical tractive forces to sea or ocean basins, with corresponding natural periods of oscillation, and in such a manner as to cause regular standing oscillations has now been considered.

It is, of course, understood that the natural configuration of the bottom and the dissipation of energy, due to friction, will greatly modify the theoretical conclusions arrived at by assuming simple geometrical forms; yet the principles are basically sound and agree remarkably well with observed facts.

It now remains to consider the effect of the earth's rotation on the behaviour of standing oscillations (sometimes called Coriolis force).

It can be demonstrated mathematically that the gyroscopic effect of the earth's rotation or component of the differential centrifugal forces—acting on any moving particle on the earth's surface—can be determined by the formula:

$$F = 2 \, m \, V \, w \, \sin l$$

Where F = gyroscopic force
      m = mass of particle in motion.
      V = velocity relative to the earth
      w = angular velocity of the earth.
      l = north latitude of particle.

This force is directed to the *right* of the motion in the northern hemisphere, to the *left* in the southern hemisphere, is zero on the equator and maximum at the poles.

If the particle is moving eastward in north latitude its velocity in space is increased, and it will tend to move southward to a parallel where the new velocity is achieved by the earth's rotation. If the movement of the particle is westward the real eastward velocity is diminished and the particle will be deflected *northward* to a parallel where such a diminished velocity is appropriate (see Fig. III, 17).

If the particle O is initially moving northward along a meridian (in north latitude) it will by virtue of its originally greater eastward velocity in space, be deflected to the right as it moves to parallels of lesser radii and diminished velocity and so is deflected eastward.

Bearing in mind this simple law for *gyroscopic deflection* we may now examine its effect on standing oscillations in a small rectangular sea in the northern hemisphere as shown in Fig. III, 18.

First to be observed is the effect of applying energy to give a simple oscillation along the major axis of the sea.

Stream rates are nil at the culmination of high and low waters but begin immediately after these instants, attaining maximum rates at the nodal line over a constant nodal cross section—midway between the times of high and low waters.

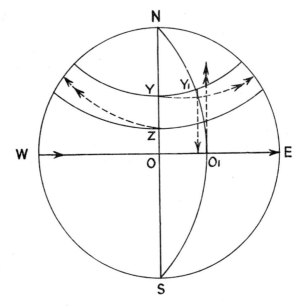

Fig. III, 17 Gyroscopic deflection on rotating earth. Earth's rotation and resultant components shown by single arrows, actual movements of particles shown by *double* arrows

O-O_1 — Movement of particle on equator due to earth's rotation. O-Y initial direction from O

Y-Y_1 — Movement of particle on parallel on N. latitude due to earth's rotation

Z & Y = Origins of particles in motion westward and eastward respectively, showing deflection

When the gyroscopic effect due to the earth's rotation is considered, the following remarkable results are observed.

Immediately following the instants of high water, an additional movement of stream to the right of the flow, across the node, occurs causing high water three hours later on the right side of the axis of flow. Six hours later high water occurs at the opposite end of the sea. The result of a complete oscillation is to produce high water along each side of the sea in succession and in an anti-clockwise direction. These observations apply to the northern hemisphere.

The effect of the earth's rotation on such a standing oscillation is to reduce the nodal line to a central point or zone around which co-tidal lines, or waves, radiate and rotate in an anti-clockwise

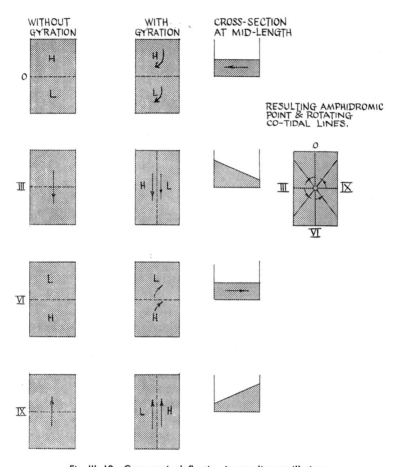

Fig. III, 18 Gyroscopic deflection in standing oscillations

direction, the range increasing with the distance from the point. This is known as an *amphidromic point,* having no range, and the system itself is known as *amphidromic system.*

Thus, in the northern hemisphere, and where *streams are appreciable* owing to relatively shallow depth, a standing oscillation is so modified by the rotation of the earth as to reduce nodal lines to points around which tidal oscillations appear to rotate. The direction of rotation is counter-*clockwise* in the

83

northern hemisphere and *clockwise* in the *southern* hemisphere, and observations broadly confirm the hypothesis to a remarkable degree (Fig. III, 10).

In the foregoing it is important to remember that gyroscopic effect is directly proportional to the horizontal velocity of streams. If we consider effects in a *small deep sea*, where the *small adjustments of level* required by the astronomical forces demand streams *of negligible velocity*, the equilibrium values will dominate gyroscopic effects and, as illustrated in Fig. III 20A, co-tidal lines

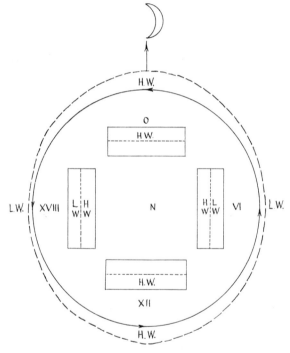

Fig. III, 19   Effect of earth's rotation in a small deep sea (A.M.T.)

will move *clockwise* around an amphidromic point in the northern hemisphere—as exemplified in the Caspian and Black Seas, and vice versa.   In such cases the range is very small (see Fig. III, 20).

Recapitulating, it has now been shown how standing oscillations are generated in the great oceans by resonance with the

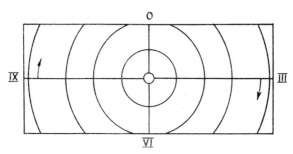

Fig. III, 20A   Resulting co-tidal lines from small deep sea shown in Fig. III, 19
(from A.M.T.)

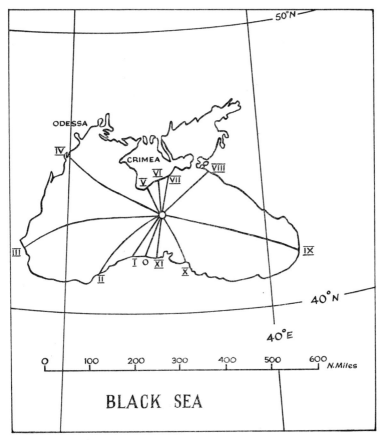

Fig. III. 20B.   Showing Cotidal lines in Black Sea
(N.B.   clockwise as equilibrium effect dominant)

astronomical tractive rhythms, the semi-diurnal and diurnal patterns being determined by the respective configurations, widths, shapes, and depths of the oceans. It has also been shown how the earth's gyration has transformed these rectilinear oscillations into amphidromic systems rotating around "no-tide" points and there is no doubt that contiguous systems must interact at their boundaries of contact. Furthermore, oceanic oscillations may be in resonance with smaller standing oscillations in gulfs. If we look at the North Sea as shown in Fig. III, 21 and assume no gyration and a physical barrier at Dover Strait, we see in the two figures on the left, a triple standing oscillation, the east-west lines being the nodal lines. The diagrams show the

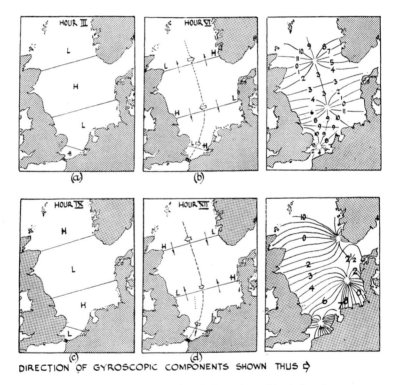

DIRECTION OF GYROSCOPIC COMPONENTS SHOWN THUS ⟡

Fig. III, 21 Standing oscillations and multiple nodes in North Sea, first assuming non-rotation earth, then adding gyroscopic components due to rotation, causing amphidromic systems somewhat resembling actuality (adapted from A.M.T.)

culmination of alternate high and low waters and the arrows indicate the streams which develop immediately after the time of such culminations and increase to maximum values at half tide level.

In the two central diagrams (b) and (d) we see the secondary nodal line caused by the deflection of the streams *to the right* due to the earth's rotation, causing elevation and depression as indicated on the east and west coasts.

The theoretical result is as shown on the top right where the system has resolved itself into three sets of co-tidal lines rotating around their respective amphidromic points. The actual co-tidal map is shown (bottom right) indicating that the theoretical conclusions, although modified by many natural features, are clearly discernible in the observed system.

In the case of the English Channel the co-tidal lines are shown in Fig. III, 12.

Again, assuming a barrier at Dover Strait, we observe that the English Channel approximates the length and depth required for resonance with a semi-diurnal oceanic oscillation.

The natural nodal line, without gyration would lie approximately between Bournemouth and Cherbourg, but it is clear that the effects of gyration cause the co-tidal lines to radiate from a "degenerate" amphidomric point north-west of the Isle of Wight.

The tidal streams are clearly deflected by Coriolis force *to the right* towards the French coast, causing the highest ranges on the south side of the Channel, the converging land contours and north/south barriers near Cherbourg and Calais causing maximum ranges at St. Malo and the mouth of Somme.

The 14 foot range curve would, in some degree, appear to constitute a secondary nodal line for the progressive transverse build-up on the French coast in the compartments to the eastward and the westward of the Cherbourg peninsula.

At 0918 G.M.T. on the days of full and change of the moon, first high water occurs at Le Havre, the tide standing approximately for three hours. At 1100 high water occurs at Spithead off the east coast of the Isle of Wight, the high water occurring between Dieppe, Boulogne, Dover and Newhaven within the next half hour up to 1120. The tidal streams then begin to run westward and the readjustment of the transverse range gradient towards Portsmouth, together with the deflection to the right due to gyration, would appear to prolong the high water in the Solent to about 1300, accentuated by shallow water effect into two manifest peaks at Southampton and Redbridge in the River Test. The Havre high water makes its first peak at about 0918 as the high water undulation passes eastward, levelling out to a prolonged stand, probably due to the continual influx into the compartment to the eastward of the Cherbourg peninsula up to 1120. Significantly, as shown by a comparison of curves in Fig. III, 7, the level at Havre begins to decline at noon between the two high waters at Southampton, the return of the oscillation causing high water from Dieppe to Calais and in this manner producing the second high water at Southampton at 1300. The description of the Southampton double high waters and Portland low waters respectively in terms of harmonic constants is complex and partially inconclusive, but will be attempted briefly under "Tidal Miscellany" in Chapter X.

SHALLOW WATER EFFECT

As the tidal pulses move in from the oceans, past the continental shelves into the arms of the sea, gulfs, estuaries and bays of relatively shoal depth, a modification of the shape of the tidal wave necessarily takes place. Tidal experts have not yet solved this problem in relation to the standing wave theory, but general results justify the assumption that roughly the same principles apply as in the distortion of a progressive wave.

In Fig. III, 22 let the harmonic curve A, B, C, D be that of a tidal wave entering an estuary. From the following formulae it will be seen that the higher positions of the wave profile above mean tide level are accelerated and those below retarded.

Mathematically expressed:

$$C = \sqrt{g} (D + 3y) \text{ or } C = (1 + 1.5\frac{y}{D} \sqrt{gD})$$

when C = rate of travel of a point on the wave profile (f.p.s.).
      D = mean depth in estuary in feet.
      y = the elevation of the point above mean level in feet.

This means that under such circumstances the period of flood tide entry will be shorter than that of the ebb, and this is normally

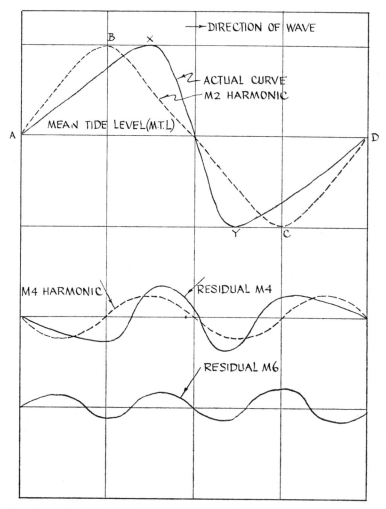

Fig. III, 22 Distortion of free progressive wave-form on encountering shallow water (from A.M.T.)

true for estuaries where there are no other complicating hydraulic factors.

The curve A X Y D illustrates this and the two residual curves obtained by subtracting the ordinates of the harmonic curve from the actual, show quarter-diurnal and sixth-diurnal constituent.

It can be shown that if g is the phase lag of the M_2 constituent the shallow water M_4 will probably have the following relationship to it:

(a) In the case of a progressive wave $2g - 90°$.

(b) In the case of a standing oscillation $2g$, or $2g + 180°$.

Whilst there are many higher species of constituents and although shallow water features at many places cannot be reproduced by their normal use, it is, however, helpful to remember that the important *quarter* and sixth *diurnal* constituents vary as the range of the primary tide increases and as the *square* and *cube* of its amplitudes respectively.

For example if the amplitude of a semi-diurnal estuarine tide is halved the quarter diurnal and sixth diurnal amplitudes would be reduced by $\frac{1}{4}$ and $\frac{1}{8}$ respectively.

This should be related to the tidal periods of Synodic, Anomalistic, and Declinational tides respectively, but in the case of the former it is generally true that the *shallow water effects at neaps are greatly reduced.*

It may be interesting to show how the relationship between M_2 and M_4 tides cause double high and low waters.

As stated above in the case of standing oscillations the relation between their phase lags was 2 (g of M_2) = g of M_4 or (g of $M_4 - 180°$).

When the M_2 and M_4 tides are in suitable phase relationship an accentuated high water or a low water stand or double low water will occur as in Figs. III, 23 and III, 24.

In addition to the phase relations necessary for the production of double high and double low waters, it can be shown mathematically that the secondary M_4 and M_6 tides, if they exist, must have amplitudes no less than $\frac{1}{4}$ and $\frac{1}{9}$ that of the primary M_2 tide respectively.

The above statement is necessarily over-simplified as higher species of tides and shallow water corrections are necessary for

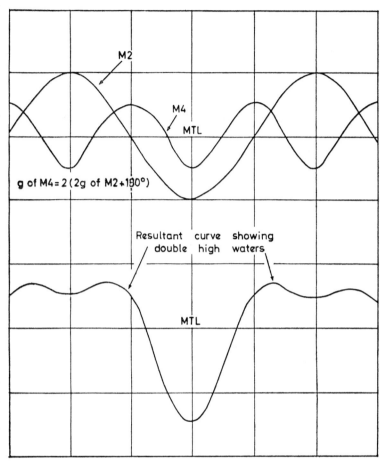

Fig. III, 23 Combination of M2 and M4 harmonic tidal curves, producing *simple* double high waters

precise prediction, but the general principles hold good as we may see in the case of the Portland and Freshwater Bay (I.O.W.) tides.

Tabulating the results of analysis we have:

	Portland	Freshwater Bay
H and g of M_2	2.07 ft. −194°	2.02 ft. −276°
H and g of M_4	0.41 ft. −030°	0.53 ft. −016°

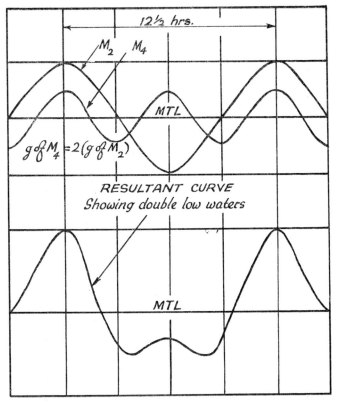

Fig. III, 24 Combinations of M_2 and M_4 harmonic tidal curves, producing simple double low waters

At Portland.

$$2 \text{ (g of } M_2) = 388° = 028° \quad H \text{ of } M_2 = 2.07 \text{ ft.}$$
$$(\text{g of } M_4) = 030° \qquad\qquad H \text{ of } M_4 = 0.41 \text{ ft.}$$

Here the conditions for double low waters are fulfilled although the ratio of amplitudes is below the theoretical requirement of $\frac{1}{4}$, but the complex situation probably demands sixth and higher diurnal species.

At Freshwater Bay.

$$2 \text{ (g of } M_2) = 552°$$
$$\text{g of } M_4 = \underline{376° \ (016° + 360°)}$$
$$\text{Difference} = \overline{176°}$$

Here the conditions for simple double high waters are fulfilled g of M4 very closely approximating the value of 2 (g of M2 —180°).

It will be noted that the phase of M_4 between Portland and the Isle of Wight varies only 14° whereas that of M_2 alters by 82°. This has been explained in theory as follows:

Assuming the tides in the English Channel to be due to a standing oscillation, the very rough nodal area on the South Coast of England lies between Christchurch and the Isle of Wight. Fig. III, 25, shows that in an area where standing oscillations occur, the location of the nodes of M_2 and M_4 waves may permit the former to alter in phase whilst that of the latter remains constant or at least with little alteration.

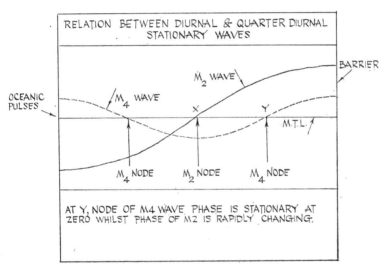

Fig. III, 25   Combination of M_2 and M_4 tidal curves, M_2 node situated between two M_4 nodes (modified from A.M.T.)

In dealing with shallow water tides and in particular the mathematical analysis of their features, which treats recorded curves of level against time as resultants of pure but complex harmonic motion, we must remember that if we go beyond the fundamental diurnal and semi-diurnal constituents we are by such devices *describing* the tidal curve rather than evaluating precise physical origins and causes in nature.

In many parts of the world, tidal behaviour in straits with two entrances is a simple hydraulic resultant of level differences between the two openings, sometimes caused by fundamentally different types of tide and on other occasions by simple range or time differences.

An example of this first instance is given by the Gut of Canso between Cape Breton Island and Nova Scotia. The range (or double the amplitude above mean tide level $= 2H$) is nearly the same at each end, but at the northern end diurnal inequality is considerable, whereas at the southern, the tide is synodic or semi-diurnal. There would thus be considerations of a hydraulic nature secondary to, but contingent upon, varying responses to the tractive forces in two different oscillating systems.

A second instance is the Solent and Southampton area. The eastern entrance off Spithead has a semi-diurnal tide with a range of over 13 feet at springs, with a prolonged stand, but the western approach off the Needles has a double high water and a range little over half of that off Spithead.

Low waters occur at nearly the same time and, on the rise, the tide runs eastward in the Solent, due to hydraulic gradients, until the Spithead level equals that off the Needles, about two hours before high water at Portsmouth. The stream then runs westward through the Needles and Solent and into Southampton Water and is running strongly off Cowes whilst still rising at Calshot and Southampton.

Fig. III, 26, illustrates this, but at Calshot and Southampton, g of M_4 is $280°$ greater than g of M_2 which reverses the double high water relations expected for a progressive wave and differs by about $90°$ from those expected in the case of a standing oscillation. Consequently we find, as we should, that the ebb tide period is a little more than half that of the flood period, a most unusual but fortunate result, probably caused by the complex secondary hydraulic factors arising from the variation of "head" in the Solent duct.

Finally one should mention the effect of tidal waves entering converging estuaries, where changes in sectional area are small within a wave-length. The results of modern theory agree with observation in demonstrating that:

(a)   Changes in *elevation* are dominantly due to changes in width.

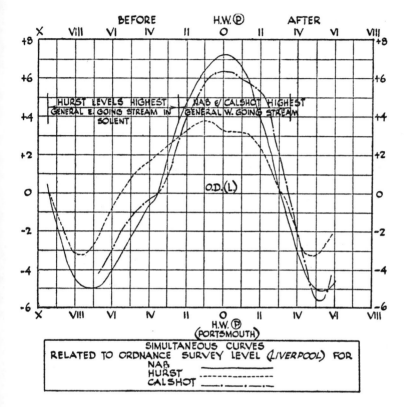

Fig. III, 26 Difference of ranges at each end of the Solent, I.O.W. and relation of tidal streams to variation and reversal of hydraulic head in amount
N.B. Low Water Datum not used as it varies

(b) Changes in the *rate* of the tidal stream are dominantly due to changes in *depth*.

These laws hold good for both standing and progressive oscillations.

It may be said that in the cases where the oceanic or external tidal pulse is exaggerated, in estuaries and channels, the two main reasons will be changes in cross-sectional width and area and also tendencies to resonance as given by the formula :

$$l \text{ (ft.)} = \tfrac{1}{2} \, T \, \sqrt{gh} \text{ or } \tfrac{1}{4} \, T \, \sqrt{gh}. \quad \text{(T in seconds, h in feet).}$$

95

Alternatively:
  Where l is length in nautical miles.
       D is depth in fathoms.
       T is period in hours.

  $l = 4.1 \text{ T } \sqrt{D}$ where l is $\frac{1}{2}$ a free progressive wave length.

  $= 2.1 \text{ T } \sqrt{D}$ where l is $\frac{1}{4}$ a free progressive wave length.

BIBLIOGRAPHY

DAWSON—Tides and Tidal Streams.

WARBURG—Tides and Tidal Streams (C.U.P. 1922).

MACMILLAN—Article on Southampton and Solent tides—Dock and Harbour Authority, February 1949.
  Also paper "Hydrography of Southampton Water" (British Association Review 1964).

REDFIELD, A. C.—The Analysis of Tidal Phenomena in Narrow Embayments (Woods Hale. Oceanographic Institution. Papers Vol. XI. No. 4. July 1950 Contribution No. 529).

DEFANT—Physical Oceanography—Pergamon Press 1961. (Vol. II).

CHAPTER FOUR

Tides and the navigator

THE NEGOTIATION of bars or shallow approaches into relatively deep-water harbours has always demanded a close practical knowledge by seamen of the behaviour of tides.

It is essential for the navigator to have a good idea of the principles underlying the leading types of tide, quite apart from the fact that accurate tabular data are now available in great detail for most parts of the world.

The great maritime nations of the West now possess many large ships having draughts of up to 50 feet, which by hydraulic effects under way may be increased by two feet or more when navigating dredged deep-water channels, with shallow side margins.

In addition an increasing number of "mammoth" oil tankers drawing over 50 feet (at rest) are entering many major terminal ports in loaded condition. In shallow water at reduced speeds of even 10 knots, increase of "draught" can amount to five feet, trim being "by the head."

For obvious economic reasons such channels are rarely dredged to take these ships at *all* states of tide and harbour authorities must provide a mean low water springs depth, which requires an assured tidal rise, to secure the safe navigation of such especially heavy draught vessels.

As the Atlantic and British tides are of a semi-diurnal character, the lunitidal interval at springs is a useful constant in these areas and the range of the tide varies more or less regularly between the days of full moon and quadrature (allowing for an Age of the Tide averaging $1\frac{1}{2}$ days).

Primary tide tables in these localities are prepared from close harmonic analysis, sometimes with triennial checks, and the precision achieved can be judged by the figures, shown overleaf,

G

obtained for the differences between prediction and observation at Liverpool, Avonmouth and London respectively.

Whilst the invaluable Admiralty Tide Tables give primary predictions with great accuracy, it is important that a seaman should be able to gauge the general effects of declination in localities such as the Pacific Ocean and its Western shores where diurnal inequality in heights means all the difference between anchoring off a harbour, or economizing in fuel to make a later arrival and entrance when the tide fully serves.

Accuracy in Prediction

		Liverpool 1937 H.W.	Avonmouth 1934 H.W.	London 1934 H.W.
Error	Less than 10 min	94%	82%	71%
	Less than 1 foot	90%	81%	87%
	Mean range	21 feet	31 feet	19 feet

Although tide tables of great precision are normally available, a competent navigator will always make intelligent deductions from visual natural phenomena and there are occasions in war and other contingencies, when this fundamental knowledge is invaluable.

In semi-diurnal areas, the moon's quite appreciably larger aspect at full indicates perigee springs and large range, and her smaller aspect at quadrature indicates apogee neaps with small range.

If, in emergency, contemporary tide tables are not available, past records may provide rough times of high water, if the Metonic cycle of 19 yrs., or its multiples are used; thus in 1952 the 1914 and 1933 data would give rough times, although the heights would be in some error owing to variations in the moon's declination and distance, and diurnal inequality.

TIDAL INFORMATION

The hydrographic departments of the leading maritime nations are generally responsible for the provision of adequate tide tables and data for the benefit of navigators.

The British Admiralty publish, in addition to the basic tide tables for the world, volumes containing non-harmonic and harmonic constants for all secondary ports. The astronomical data for use with the Admiralty method of prediction and also the values of the four basic constituents M_2, S_2, K_1 and O_1, are included in the tide tables for the different regions of the world.

Volume III of the Admiralty Tide Tables deals especially with the problems of analysis and tidal prediction.

It is claimed for the Admiralty method of prediction that the tidal levels corrected for shallow water effect are sufficiently accurate for the general purposes of navigation, the possible errors not exceeding 1/10 the range.

Modern navigators are indeed fortunate in having ample means for predicting with fair accuracy the curve of heights for any period or time at any of the ports for which the four harmonic constituents are available. It must, however, be noted that the method is *not* satisfactory for the British Isles on account of the large shallow water effects. Where such conditions exist, non-harmonic constants using suitable standard ports give most reliable results, subject of course to meteorological corrections.

On all Admiralty charts, fundamental local tidal information is given, including neap and spring ranges, the connection of datum to shore levels and in particular land survey level planes.

Soundings are all shown reduced to low water datum of soundings and it can be said with confidence that the charted presentation indicates contours and soundings for the least depths to be experienced, apart from unusually low spring low water levels.

Finally it is to be noted that the hydrographic charts published by the British Admiralty show tables for "compartments" indicating the direction and rate of streams from hour to hour, for various positions indicated by numbers or letters and related to times of local high water, where this is possible.

TIDAL NAVIGATION

In those localities where tidal ranges and streams are great and deep draught commerce in consequence critically affected, the tide is generally of a semi-diurnal type and the times of tidal streams, and indeed tidal times generally, can be predicted with fair enough accuracy for navigational allowances.

Consequently, when navigating areas like the English Channel, the course to steer, hour by hour, to counteract varying tidal streams can be determined by a simple triangle of forces allowing for the direction found in the tidal compartment for the required time and the rate, interpolated between spring and neap values, combined with the ship's course and speed through the water.

Practical navigators make much use of the times of covering or uncovering of well-known rocks for tidal levels and also pay great attention to the direction in which light-vessels are riding both by day and by night.

Hazardous operations with small clearances *are not attempted on falling tides by prudent seamen*, nor indeed on occasions when synodic, semi-diurnal, tides are reducing their ranges after springs. Few casualties carry more opprobrium among seamen than that of being "neaped" before quadrature and being obliged to "ebb out" and wait, as a monument of indiscretion, for about ten days, until the ranges again build up towards springs! In regions where tides are diurnal, with ranges of up to 10 ft. it is important to realise that "neaping" is rather a misnomer, as maximum ranges are related to the maximum lunar declination rather than syzygies.

Meteorological effects

The subject will be dealt with in some detail in a later chapter but it is important that navigators consider the effect of barometric pressure and winds upon the tidal systems within which they are navigating. Generally speaking these effects are greater at neaps, or times of lesser ranges, but with a high barometer and strong winds, levels can be considerably lowered and the turn of the tide in straits and channels materially altered, even in semi-diurnal regions where ranges are considerable.

Freshet effects in estuaries

An interesting phenomenon occurs in estuaries situated, as nearly all are, at the mouth of rivers. The fresh water flow particularly during seasons of heavy rains, spreads in a layer above the more salt water of the estuary and particularly in the upper reaches where dredged approaches to docks are located.

In Southampton Water, for example, off the Dock approaches, this layer extends downwards from the surface from 4-7 feet attaining a rate approaching one knot at slack water. On the flood tide, before the rate of the incoming salt water attains maximum values, the surface stream is outgoing and dominantly affects the handling of shallow draught craft such as tugs, tenders, dredgers, hoppers etc. Surface indications, the flow past buoys for example, are very misleading to those handling the deeper draught ships drawing say over 30 feet, which are affected dominantly by the sub-surface flood stream.

In such cases, the deeper vessel is manoeuvring in accordance with the sub-surface flow, which is in phase with the vertical rise and contrary to the surface indications, whereas the attendant tugs disregard tide table data and are handled in accordance with the surface current, derived from the fresh-water outflow.

This is a parallel, on a major scale, to the device of the Bosphorus fishermen, who lower a drogue into the sub-surface streams when they desire to work up against the surface stream without undue effort. Their experience has been not without profit to British submarine commanders navigating the same area.

BIBLIOGRAPHY

Any work on Hydrographic Surveying.
Any work on Navigation.
MARMER—The Tide.
DARWIN—The Tides.

CHAPTER FIVE

Tides and the local observer

STANDARD PORTS

AT ALL the major ports of the world and at many other localities, continuous and accurate observations, carefully reduced to suitable tidal datums, connected to land survey planes, have provided the tidal observer with an adequate basis for close analysis and prediction.

These stations are known as primary or *standard* ports, and predictions at secondary stations, near and depending upon them are usually made by systems of tidal differences and constants.

Before the methods of harmonic analysis came into general use, a statistical method of analysis using long series of high and low water times and heights, with astronomical correlations based upon the equilibrium tide, was commonly employed, methods being handed down from father to son.

Today, a 29 day series of continuous hourly height observations provides an adequate basis for a reasonably good preliminary harmonic analysis for ports of minor importance, although major seasonal and meteorological variations in mean sea level can be covered only by observations extending over a period of *at least one solar year*.

Where continuous automatic tidal recordings are taken, as is the case at all major ports, analysis over a long cycle of years, ideally over the "exhaustive" period of the Metonic 19 year cycle, provides the tidal analyst with the material for first-class mathematical prediction. The evaluation of seasonal changes in Mean Sea Level and short period changes of level due to meteorological factors can then be achieved. For such standard ports predictions for the times of culmination of single and double high and low waters, are available in all the leading tide tables of the world.

SECONDARY PORTS

Clustered around standard ports are the essential secondary ports and stations, predictions for which are connected with those for standard ports by simple time and height differences, commonly but incorrectly called "constants." For the British Isles the *standard* port predictions are given in Vol. I of the Admiralty Tide Tables and the data for secondary ports in the form of tidal differences are included in Part II.

Such non-harmonic tidal differences cannot be relied upon for consistently accurate results throughout the lunar month unless:

(a) The time difference between the phase lags of corresponding major harmonic constituents is nearly the same for them all.

(b) The amplitude ratios of corresponding constituents are nearly the same for them all.

For example, the major constituents used in the "Admiralty" method are M_2, S_2, K_1, and O_1, with hourly speed numbers of $29°$, $30°$, $15°$ and $14°$ respectively.

Tabulating these values for a hypothetical standard and secondary port respectively we have, say:

	Semi-diurnal				Diurnal			
	(M_2)		(S_2)		(K_1)		(O_1)	
	Phase Lag	H	Phase Lag	H	Phase Lag	H	Phase Lag	H
Standard	020°	3.0′	050°	1.0′	100°	2.0′	130°	1.0′
Secondary	049°	6.0′	080°	2.0′	115°	4.0′	144°	2.0′
Difference	29°	3.0′	30°	1.0[1]	15°	2.0′	14°	1.0′

Here we see that the *time* difference in the case of all the constituents is $+0100$ hours and the amplitude (H) ratio a constant 2.0. The relationship is, therefore, constant throughout the lunar cycle and the time and height differences applied to the

Standard port will agree with normal observations or predictions made by rigorous harmonic methods.

Such a precise relationship is rarely found, but where it is *approximately* true, time and height differences can give fair results.

If either the diurnal or semi-diurnal height values (H) are negligibly small, the time and height differences will give reasonable accuracy over the lunar cycle if the phase relationship of the larger two constituents is good.

Also if the diurnal (H) values are relatively small, spring time and height differences will be reasonably constant.

The above reasoning confirms the opinion of Dr. Bell Dawson that tidal time and height differences apply between tides of the leading Synodic Declinational, and Anomalistic types respectively. He has stated: "In our Canadian work we have been able to show that it is often possible to produce satisfactory tide tables by means of a constant difference in time from a port in a distant ocean providing the type of tide is the same.

For example, the time of high water at Nelson (which will be the railway terminal at Hudson Bay) can be computed from a port in the North sea. The tide in Miramichi Bay is of the same type as in the Strait of Georgia on the Pacific, except that the tide curve is inverted, and accordingly low water in Miramichi Bay shows a constant difference with high water in the Strait of Georgia, although these places are on the opposite coasts of North America. As the tide in the Hudson Strait is of the Anomalistic type, just as in the Bay of Fundy, both high and low water there can be computed from the tide tables for St. John, New Brunswick, which is 1,200 miles to the south.

These correlations result from investigations carried out to save the expense of erecting permanently equipped tidal stations at remote localities, since by the methods referred to, adequate data can be obtained from a restricted series of observations in the summer season, but they corroborate the view that a proper classification of the tides should enable a limited number of typical ones to be found which would represent the tides of the whole world adequately. This question is discussed in a paper by the author entitled "Variation in the leading features of the tide in different regions" (Journal R.A.S., Canada Vol. I, p. 213).

THE LOCAL TIDE GAUGE

Valuable information can be obtained from a monthly series of continuous hourly readings of a local visual gauge erected on a stable pile or structure, sheltered from wave action by prevailing winds and at a point that does not dry out at extreme low waters. The zero of such a gauge should be connected by levelling to a near and permanent plane surface such as a quay or rock, but also to "bench" or reference marks established by official land survey authorities by methods of precise levelling.

If it is desired to erect a temporary gauge on a seashore, a tide pole should be driven securely and mauled down hard by chain-stropped wedging just outside water level at lower low water springs. The visual tide board can then be set with zero to waterline. The observer can then roughly determine the extraordinary and ordinary spring ranges by seeking the obvious markings on the near shore, settling his eye literally at these levels and reading the gauge where the *sea* horizon intersects it. The heights above Mean Tide Level will be semi-ranges.

This plane is depressed only by $\sqrt{H}$, in minutes of arc, below the true horizontal plane (where H = height of eye in feet) and is generally negligible, except where range is excessive (Fig. V, 1). Use of shore horizon will of course need standard correction if close.

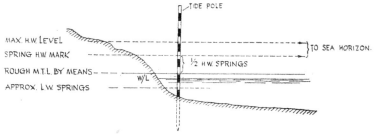

Fig. V, I   Rough method of levelling by sea horizon to determine Spring range and establish a provisional L.W. datum of soundings

A month's continuous hourly observations at such a site, with careful reading and timekeeping, would provide the tidal analyst with adequate data for predictions normally accurate enough for the purpose of engineering works or navigational predictions.

INTERMEDIATE TIDAL LEVELS BETWEEN HIGH AND LOW WATERS

Where access to ports, harbours and landing hards at low water is restricted near low water times by the draughts of the ships using them, it is important to know the intermediate levels between high and low water at which approach and entry are safe.

Where diurnal inequality is small as in the North Atlantic area generally, the simplest way of doing this is to tabulate mean observed curves for every half foot of range and use the assumption that the shape of any curve depends upon its range.

If the values for the rise above predicted low water are applied from the curve appropriate to the range, the results—apart from meteorological disturbances—should be reasonably good.

This method is used for the complicated Southampton tides with excellent results that can be relied upon by those operating large ships drawing up to 50 feet (see Table 1).

Curves are also tabulated on this principle in Vol. 1 of the British Admiralty Tide Tables for the entire area lying between Swanage and Selsey Bill, including Spithead and the Solent, thus providing a reliable arrangement of complicated data in a small compass.

Since 1964 the British Admiralty Tide Tables (Vol. 1—European Waters) have included valuable *diagrams* showing the mean tidal curves for typical Springs and Neaps at Standard Ports in the United Kingdom.

By using these curves and factors appropriate to the time interval from the nearest predicted High Water, the range multiplied by the factor will give the increment required to be added to the level of the predicted Low Water to give the intermediate height of the tide at any selected time.

The results, whilst approximate and subject of course to meteorological perturbations, are of much greater accuracy than those derived from methods that assumed the simple semi-diurnal curves around the British Isles to approximate cosine values.

Used with adequate cautionary margins—including meteorological corrections and allowing for "settlement" of large ships in shallow channels of restricted width—the results provided by these factors and curves are well within the order of accuracy required by navigators using major terminals of the United Kingdom.

TOWN QUAY REDUCTION TABLE (Heights in feet and decimals above Low Water, Town Quay). TIDE LETTER FOR DAY (from Tables).

Time from L.W.	A	B	C	D	E	F	G	H	J	K	L	M	N
Before low water													
3½ hours	4.0	5.0	5.5	5.8	6.3	6.8	7.3	7.8	8.3	8.7	9.3	9.7	10.2
3 hours	3.8	4.8	5.2	5.3	5.7	6.0	6.7	7.4	7.9	8.4	8.9	9.4	9.9
2½ hours	3.5	4.2	4.3	4.6	5.0	5.3	5.7	6.4	6.8	7.4	7.9	8.5	9.0
2 hours	2.9	3.3	3.4	3.5	3.8	4.1	4.5	4.9	5.4	5.9	6.3	6.8	7.3
1½ hours	1.8	1.9	2.0	2.3	2.5	2.7	2.8	3.3	3.6	3.9	4.2	4.6	4.8
1 hour	0.8	0.8	0.8	1.0	1.0	1.2	1.3	1.4	1.6	1.7	2.0	2.3	2.5
0½ hour	0.3	0.3	0.3	0.3	0.3	0.3	0.3	0.4	0.4	0.4	0.4	0.4	0.5
Low water	0.0	0.0	0.0	0.0	0.0	0.0	0.0	0.0	0.0	0.0	0.0	0.0	0.0
After low water:													
0½ hour	0.2	0.1	0.1	0.2	0.2	0.2	0.2	0.3	0.3	0.4	0.4	0.5	0.5
1 hour	0.3	0.4	0.4	0.5	0.6	0.7	0.7	0.8	0.8	1.0	1.1	1.3	1.5
1½ hours	0.6	0.7	0.8	0.8	0.9	1.0	1.2	1.3	1.5	1.7	1.8	2.0	2.3
2 hours	0.7	0.8	0.8	0.9	1.0	1.1	1.3	1.6	1.7	2.0	2.5	2.8	3.0
2½ hours	0.8	0.9	0.9	1.0	1.1	1.2	1.5	1.7	1.9	2.6	2.8	3.2	3.5
3 hours	1.0	1.1	1.2	1.2	1.3	1.5	1.7	1.8	2.1	2.9	3.1	3.6	3.9
3½ hours	1.2	1.5	1.5	1.6	1.7	1.9	2.0	2.2	2.8	3.3	3.6	3.9	4.2
4 hours	1.5	1.7	1.8	1.8	1.9	2.0	2.4	2.9	3.3	3.6	3.9	4.2	4.5
4½ hours	1.7	1.9	2.0	2.2	2.4	2.7	3.0	3.3	3.7	4.0	4.3	4.7	5.0
5 hours	2.3	2.6	2.7	2.9	3.2	3.5	3.9	4.4	5.0	5.4	5.8	6.2	6.5
5½ hours	2.9	3.4	3.8	3.9	4.2	4.6	5.0	5.5	6.0	6.5	7.0	7.6	8.1
6 hours	3.2	3.9	4.4	4.6	5.4	6.0	6.6	7.1	7.7	8.1	8.6	9.1	9.6
6½ hours	3.7	4.4	4.9	5.5	6.0	6.7	7.2	7.7	8.2	8.8	9.3	9.8	10.3

The "Young Flood" bracket label appears spanning the *After low water* rows.

Time from L.W.	O	P	Q	R	S	T	V	W	X	Y	Z
Before low water:											
3½ hours	10.7	11.2	11.7	12.2	12.7	13.3	13.8	14.3	14.8	15.3	15.8
3 hours	10.4	10.9	11.4	11.9	12.3	12.8	13.3	13.8	14.2	14.4	15.2
2½ hours	9.5	10.0	10.5	10.9	11.4	11.8	12.2	12.7	13.1	13.5	13.9
2 hours	7.7	8.1	8.5	8.9	9.3	9.7	10.1	10.5	10.9	11.3	11.7
1½ hours	5.1	5.4	5.7	6.0	6.3	6.6	6.9	7.2	7.4	7.7	8.0
1 hour	2.8	3.0	3.1	3.3	3.4	3.6	3.7	3.8	4.0	4.1	4.2
0½ hour	0.5	0.6	0.7	0.8	0.9	1.0	1.1	1.1	1.2	1.3	1.4
Low water	0.0	0.0	0.0	0.0	0.0	0.0	0.0	0.0	0.0	0.0	0.0
After low water:											
0½ hour	0.6	0.6	0.7	0.8	0.9	0.9	0.9	0.9	0.9	1.0	1.0
1 hour	1.6	1.8	1.9	2.2	2.2	2.3	2.4	2.6	2.7	2.8	2.9
1½ hours	2.5	2.8	3.0	3.2	3.4	3.6	3.8	4.0	4.3	4.5	4.7
2 hours	3.3	3.7	3.9	4.1	4.3	4.5	4.9	5.2	5.4	5.6	5.8
2½ hours	3.7	4.1	4.4	4.5	4.7	4.9	5.5	5.8	6.1	6.4	6.7
3 hours	4.2	4.5	4.7	5.0	5.2	5.5	5.7	6.1	6.4	6.7	7.0
3½ hours	4.5	4.7	5.0	5.3	5.5	5.7	6.0	6.4	6.7	7.0	7.3
4 hours	4.8	5.1	5.3	5.6	5.9	6.0	6.2	6.8	7.1	7.4	7.7
4½ hours	5.3	5.6	5.8	6.1	6.5	6.7	7.0	7.3	7.7	8.0	8.3
5 hours	6.8	7.2	7.6	8.0	8.4	8.7	9.2	9.6	10.1	10.5	10.9
5½ hours	8.6	9.0	9.5	9.9	10.2	10.6	11.4	11.9	12.4	12.9	13.4
6 hours	10.2	10.7	11.2	11.7	12.2	12.7	13.2	13.7	14.2	14.7	15.2
6½ hours	10.8	11.3	11.8	12.4	12.9	13.4	13.9	14.4	14.9	15.4	15.9

The "Young Flood" bracket label appears spanning the *After low water* rows.

Table 1
Town Quay reduction Table (Southampton)

Where the *diurnal* constituents are appreciable, recourse must be had to results from predicting machines or computers which will, of course, give a fairly high order of accuracy.

An alternative system for such areas is the use of the "Admiralty" method of prediction which will now be described briefly.

THE "ADMIRALTY" METHOD OF LOCAL PREDICTION

The practical results of harmonic analysis at many stations have demonstrated the following features:

(a) The equilibrium relations of constituents, with approximately equal speeds, are to a greater or less degree reflected in the actual constituents found by rigorous analysis.

(b) Observed tides rarely approximate to equilibrium relationships because the magnitude of the response of given areas and depths of sea depends not only upon the value of the generating forces, but also upon the degree of resonance of their periodicities. Hence if an area of sea has a diurnal period tractive forces will stimulate a diurnal resonance which will build up beyond the equilibrium values. If, on the other hand, conditions nearer a 12 hour, or semi-diurnal period of oscillation, are present, the response evoked by the more rapid semi-diurnal generating forces will correspondingly amplify equilibrium values. Consequently the diurnal and semi-diurnal tides must be treated separately if their combined values in relation to the astronomical forces are to be adequately expressed.

(c) The amplitudes of the solar and lunar semi-diurnal constituents S_2 and M_2 respectively do not invariably in nature have the ratio $0.46 : 1$ and there are occasions when the amplitude of the solar constituent S_2 is greater than the lunar M_2.

This may be due in some measure to a critical and precise synchronism between the natural period of oscillation of particular marine areas and the solar periodicity of 12 hours, which causes a predominant response.

(d) In grouping the semi-diurnal and diurnal tidal responses separately, it is found that there is a corresponding natural relationship between the two groups of astronomical generating forces, which, without serious error, can be expressed practically and comprehensively by the basic use of the constituents M_2, S_2, K_1, O_1, with modifications.

(e) The variation in amplitude/ratio noted in (b) and (c) is often accompanied by variation in phase lag.

The Admiralty method is, therefore, an ingenious device for making use of the harmonic analysis of any given place as expressed by the four basic constituents M_2, S_2, K_1 and O_1, modifying them to include a wide range of constituents and adjusting them to astronomical conditions by equilibrium concepts.

In simple harmonic prediction, we have seen that the height of any given constituent above sea level is given by $H \cos (nt - g)$ where H = height in feet

$\qquad$ n = speed in degrees per hour or speed number

$\qquad$ t = time in hours

$\qquad$ g = lag of phase behind phase of equilibrium constituent at Greenwich.

In the Admiralty method

$\qquad$ g is replaced by $g + b + c$

$\qquad$ H is replaced by B.C.H.

where b = an angle depending upon the date

$\qquad$ c = an angle depending approximately upon the time of the moon's transit

$\qquad$ B = a factor depending upon the date

$\qquad$ C = a factor depending upon the moon's distance.

These symbols comprehend a simplification of the astronomical arguments by deriving them all from the relations of the transits of the sun and moon, and the date. Hence the formula for the height in the Admiralty method is:

$$B \, C \, H \cos (nt - g - b - c).$$

After the modification of the constituents the semi-diurnal and diurnal constituents are respectively paired and compounded into a single semi-diurnal and a single diurnal constituent, results being modified by shallow water corrections and seasonal sea level variations and finally plotted as a curve of heights.

Many simplifications in the process of computation have been achieved in the Tidal Branch of the Hydrographic Department of the Admiralty and a 24 hour curve can be plotted in half an hour by using the various tables and diagrams supplied to seamen which can be obtained from any Admiralty Chart agent.

Furthermore, the method is applicable to tidal streams, and values corresponding to the four basic harmonic constituents are being tabulated for an increasing number of sites.

It is necessary to state, however, that neither the ordinary harmonic, nor the Admiralty method of prediction, are adequate for the prediction of accurate tidal curves for the coasts of the British Isles on account of large shallow water effects which require special and complicated treatment involving the use of higher species than the diurnal or semi-diurnal constituents and also special shallow water corrections.

Apart from this limitation, the Admiralty data, available to all seamen, engineers, and scientists, enable a curve of heights to be drawn with rapidity and fair accuracy for any of these increasingly numerous tidal stations for which the basic constituents are tabulated and where the quarter, sixth, diurnal and higher species of constituents are small in amplitude.

BIBLIOGRAPHY

DAWSON—Tides and Tidal Streams.
Admiralty Tide Tables.
Admiralty Manual of Tides.

Tides and the weather

THE OCCURRENCE of extreme tides is of paramount importance to navigators, civil engineers and conservancy officers responsible for approaches to harbours. Where harmonic constituents are available, the maximum possible *astronomical* high and low water values are respectively given by the following approximate formulae, where the diurnal tide is small.

Max. H.W. height = Mean Sea Level +
$$1.2 \text{ (H of } M_2 + \text{H of } S_2 + \text{H of } K_2)$$
Min. L.W. height = Mean Sea Level −
$$1.2 \text{ (H of } M_2 + \text{H of } S_2 + \text{H of } K_2)$$
The Admiralty Tide tables now give these values for U.K.

It is important that statistics of phenomenal tides be obtained from the inhabitants of any area before deciding upon the maximum heights of piers, quays and banks. Clearly such maximum values are due to the raising and lowering of adjacent mean sea or tide level by meteorological factors and any wave action must be imposed upon the maximum level predicted if flooding is

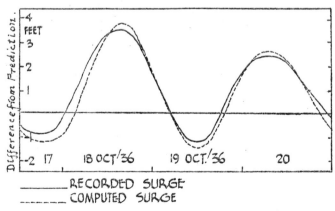

Fig. VI, I   Computed and actual curves of Southend surge 17-20 October 1936
(A.M.T. Modified)

to be considered. Storm surges have, since the disastrous Thames flooding in 1928, been closely investigated by the Liverpool Tidal Institute and a technique for prediction has been worked out with some success (see Fig. VI, 1).

At Sheerness levels have attained 5 feet above prediction. On 5 October 1869, at perigee springs the level of the water in Cumberland basin in the Bay of Fundy was raised 6.2 feet above prediction. At Quebec on 20 November 1914, levels rose 5.4 feet above prediction.

In all these cases gales and low barometric pressure prevailed.

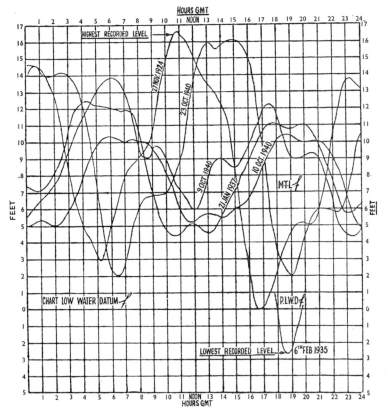

Fig. VI, 2 Abnormal curves recorded at Southampton due to meteorological surges (by permission of the Southampton Harbour Board)

On other occasions the lowering of levels, particularly at low water springs, has embarrassed navigators in certain localities.

On 6 February 1935, at Southampton Town Quay, for example, low water fell to 2 feet 8 inches below low water springs, or 1.9 feet below prediction. (Fig. VI, 2).

In this case the barometric pressure was high. Statistics show very clearly that apart from abnormal seismic surges similar to the classical case of the Lisbon earthquake in 1755, there are three factors causing that build-up of mean sea level which temporarily raises the mean tide level of the oscillating systems found in gulfs, estuaries and harbours, without necessarily altering the shape and amplitude of the tidal curve. The phenomenal and disastrous flooding in the North Sea coasts in January 1953 has led the Admiralty to establish a storm surge warning system at Dunstable where formulae devised by tidal physicists, combined with a system of tide gauge readings, are used to predict the imminence of abnormal flooding. Extensive civil engineering works were necessitated by this catastrophe in which many lives were lost. (Fig. VI, 3).

(a) Atmospheric pressure

Considered statistically the "equilibrium relation" causes the sea to behave like an inverted water barometer, 13 inches alteration of sea level being equivalent to 1 inch of mercury.

As 1.5 inches is the maximum deviation of the barometer pressure from normal we may expect the maximum elevation or depression of sea level *from this cause* to be less than 20 inches even if it extends over a very large area of sea.

(b) The movement of meteorological tide generating forces

We may consider these disturbing forces as moving over areas of water with natural periods of oscillation determined by their size, shape, depth and configuration.

In the case of a small sea, a steep pressure gradient impressed and suddenly removed might set up a standing oscillation of a period appropriate to its dimensions.

In the case of a travelling pressure system, if the speed of the system is critical, a response similar to that evoked by other tide generating systems can occur.

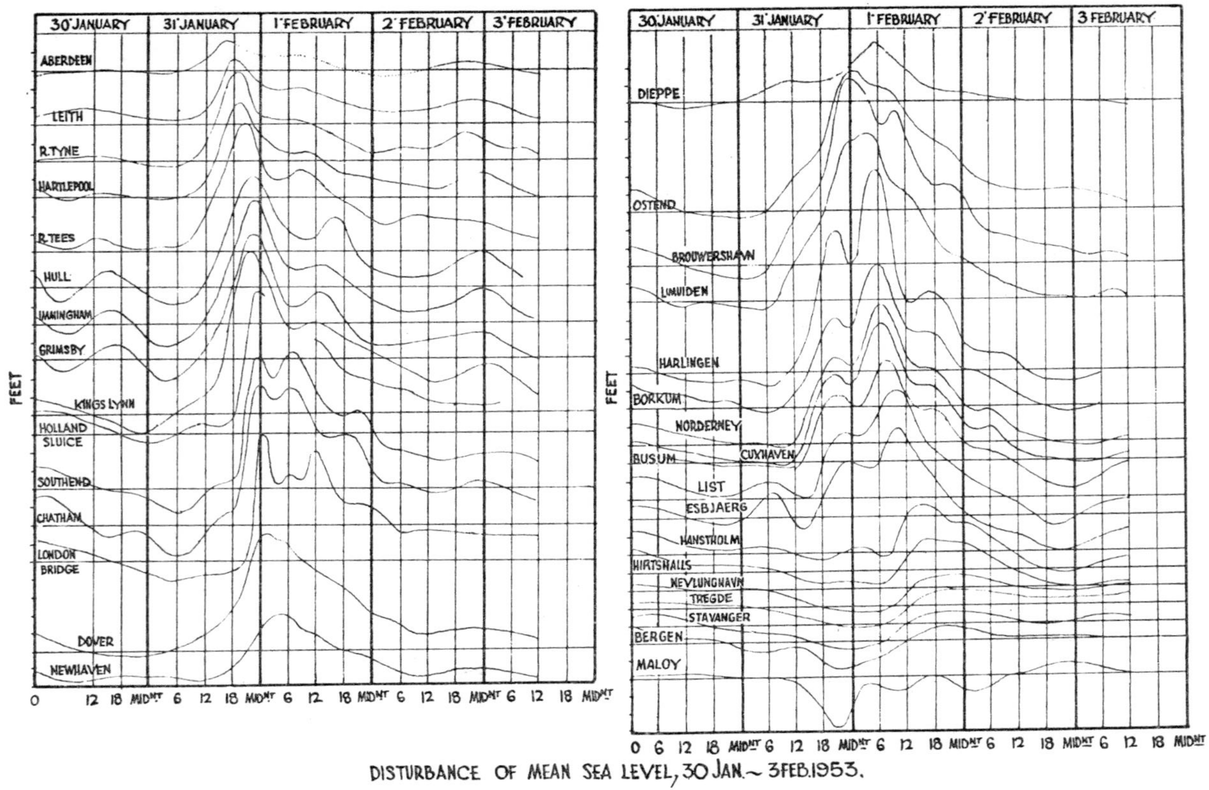

DISTURBANCE OF MEAN SEA LEVEL, 30 JAN. ~ 3 FEB. 1953.

Fig. VI, 3   Shows progress of phenomenal storm surge in North Sea, January 31-1 February 1953 (by permission of R. Society)

It can be shown that the elevation of sea level at any place resulting from such a moving pressure system can *in theory* be qualitatively expressed in the following formulae:

$$y = \frac{13\,(29.8 - P)}{1 - C^2/gD}$$

Where y = elevation of sea surface in feet
      C = the speed of the disturbance in feet per second
      D = mean depth of water in feet
      P = corrected barometric height in inches.

The formula may be simplified by using the value:

$$\frac{C_2}{gD} = \frac{K^2}{68\,D}$$

Where K = speed in knots of the pressure system
      D = depth in fathoms.

The formula shows that where the speed of travel in knots of the pressure disturbance approaches $\sqrt{gh}$ or $8.23 \times \sqrt{\text{depth in fathoms}}$, being the rate of travel of a free oscillation, *resonance will occur* and the elevation of the sea will *exceed the statical elevation.* For example, if a low pressure disturbance is travelling at the rate of 50 knots over a sea 50 fathoms deep and at any given point the barometer stands at 27.8 inches, the elevation of the sea surface in feet would be, in theory:

$$y = \frac{13\,(29.8 - P)}{1 - \dfrac{K^2}{68\,D}}$$

$$= \frac{13 \times (29.8 - 27.8)}{1 - \dfrac{50^2}{68 \times 50}}$$

$$= \frac{26}{1 - \dfrac{50}{68}}$$

$$= \frac{26 \times 68}{18} \text{ (approx.)}$$

$$= 98 \text{ inches.}$$

The formulae given *obviously neglects frictional forces*, otherwise when a pressure disturbance achieved resonance the denominator would become zero and the elevations infinitely large, which is absurd. On the other hand, the use of the expression will indicate conditions likely to lead to *unduly large* elevations or depressions in the sea surface.

In this connection, it is useful to note the following statistics of storms travelling at more than 30 knots over a period of 30 years:

25	travelled at	31-35 knots
14	,,	36-40 ,,
11	,,	41-45 ,,
4	,,	46-50 ,,
3	,,	51-55 ,,
2	,,	56-60 ,,
1	,,	61 ,,

It will be noted that the maximum rate of travel is near the rate of a progressive wave in 50 fathoms. Frequently a long prevailing and stationary depression in the North Atlantic releases a secondary depression moving swiftly towards the British coasts. It is under such circumstances that prevailing statical elevations accentuated by wind are suddenly increased and it is, therefore, profitable for those in charge of ports and harbours in the English and Bristol Channels, and elsewhere on our west coasts, to keep a careful check on weather maps for these features.

Approximate local tables can be prepared from past records by plotting the divergence from the equilibrium elevation for wind strengths of 30-40 knots and over, on separate graphs for, say, each 30° of wind direction. Tables of averages can thus be prepared to indicate possibilities and the conditions for probable local maxima (see Table 2).

(c) The effect of wind

The effect of strong winds upon the sea or water surface is to communicate energy to it by friction, depending upon the relative viscosities of air and water. The subject is more than usually complicated and relatively little is known upon which to base a truly comprehensive theory. The result of some observations and researches indicates that with "contact" wind values of over 20 knots, a surface drift of 1/30th of wind speed is a close approximation.

(A) Barometer Table		(B) Wind Table		
Barometer	Correction ft.	Direction	Fresh Winds	Heavy Gale
28.50	+2.6	N.	−0.7	−1.5
28.75	+2.3	N.E.	−0.7	−1.5
29.00	+2.0	E.	−0.3	−1.0
29.25	+1.7	S.E.	−0.2	−0.5
29.50	+1.2	S.	0.0	0.0
29.75	+0.7	S.W.	0.0	0.0
		W.	0.0	0.0
30.00	+0.2	N.W.	−0.3	−1.0
30.25	−0.5			
30.50	−1.2			
30.75	−1.8			

Table 2
Meteorological correction tables computed for Southampton

Over 30.00″ with very strong N.E. gale low water may fall to 2.0 feet below prediction in very exceptional cases.

Corrections from Tables (A) and (B) to be applied to predicted heights. The corrections are given in feet and decimals (+) or (−) to heights predicted in the Main Tables or derived from the Reduction Tables. The approximate corrections given in this Table are average figures based upon the official predictions for previous years.

The "Heavy Gale" column gives maximum values, and should certainly be used when the correction is minus, in order that a safe margin be given.

(The Town Quay and Calshot Reductions Tables and matter relating thereto are *Copyright* by the Southampton Harbour Board.)

In deep water, cyclonic disturbances may cause the movement of vast quantities of water; changes in mean level are relatively small but there is often considerable turbulence with waves, some of which attain heights of 40-50 feet.

Free oscillations radiating from such disturbances accompanied by reactions of the sea-bottom discernible on far distant seismographs and which cause appreciable seiches, account for the premonitory offshore swells so long regarded by fishermen, seamen, (and even sea birds and fishes) as harbingers of approaching storms.

In deep water, according to Ekman, the earth's gyration causes the surface drift to be inclined 45° to the right of a steady wind in the Northern hemisphere and 45° to the left in the Southern hemisphere.

Near the coasts, frictional effect reduces this value to about 20°. In estuaries, bays and gulfs of simple longitudinal shape, when the wind direction is along the axis, levels at the head are reduced by winds blowing towards the mouth or increased when blowing in, especially in the latter case, if, as is usual, the cross-section decreases.

At neap tides the effect of wind on elevation is generally greater than at springs when the kinetic energy due to tidal pulses dominates, to a great degree, any standing oscillations produced by other causes. It is also true that surges have greater amplitude at high water than at low.

In the North Sea the natural period of oscillation is about 36 hours between recurring high or low levels. If a strong and steady wind has raised sea level in one locality and then quickly changes by about 180° an oscillation is imposed on the normal tidal regime and if maxima coincide, serious flooding may occur in the Thames and other areas.

A depression moving eastwards from Northern Ireland towards Scandinavia or Denmark would progressively cause strong winds from S.-S.S.W. *reducing* North Sea levels subsequently changing to winds from N. and N.N.W. causing *increasing* levels in the North Sea* (see Fig. VI, 3A).

The Catastrophic flooding on the North Sea coastal areas in January 1953 came about several years after this paragraph was written (vide *Waves & Tides*, Russell & Macmillan, Hutchinson 1952.

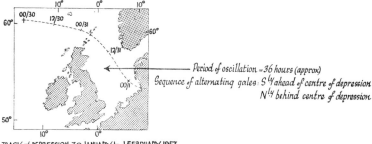

Period of oscillation = 36 hours (approx)
Sequence of alternating gales: S'ly ahead of centre of depression
N'ly behind centre of depression

TRACK of DEPRESSION, 30 JANUARY to 1 FEBRUARY 1953

Fig. 3A

If this movement of such a pressure system with sustained gradients, occupied a period of 18 hours the change in wind direction from southerly to northerly would coincide with a natural semi-oscillation, causing very violent surges, especially if synchronizing with the time of high water.

The Lake of Geneva affords an interesting example of standing oscillations in an enclosed basin set in motion by winds, air-pressure gradients, or perhaps on some occasions local seismic movements of the bed of the lake.

Vaucher, in the eighteenth century, gives an account of a major oscillation or seiche in the year 1600 when the levels had a range of over 3 feet and Forel has given several most interesting papers on his detailed observations during the years 1875-1885 including formulae for the computation of seiches.

The Lake is crescent-shaped, or variable depth, and is remarkable for a dominant "seiche longitudinal" and also "seiches transversales," the periods being about 73 and 10 minutes, respectively.

The length of Lake Geneva is 45 miles and depths range between 80 and 170 fathoms.

It is interesting to deduce the average depths required to give these observed periods from the formula:

$$L = 4.1 \, T \, \sqrt{D}$$

$$\text{or} \quad D = \left(\frac{L}{4.1 \, T}\right)^2 \qquad D = \text{mean depth in fathoms}$$

119

or (taking P in minutes)

$$D = \left(\frac{60\,L}{4.1\,T}\right)^2 \qquad L = \text{length in nautical miles.}$$

Taking length and transverse width as respectively 38 and 8½ miles respectively:

(a) Longitudinal D (fathoms) $= \left(\dfrac{60 \times 38}{4.1 \times 73}\right)^2$

$\qquad\qquad\qquad\qquad\qquad = 58$ fathoms (nearly)

(b) Transverse D $\qquad\qquad = \left(\dfrac{60 \times 8.5}{4.1 \times 10}\right)^2$

$\qquad\qquad\qquad\qquad\qquad = 155$ fathoms (nearly).

Recollecting the curved shape and varying depths of the Lake over its entire length, the calculated depth for the longitudinal period appears to be roughly in accord with nature.

The transverse value agrees closely with depths over the transverse section at mid-length, and the unobstructed passage of the wave would account for such close agreement between theory and nature.

BIBLIOGRAPHY

DR. DOODSON, F. R. S. and MR. R. J. CORKAN, various papers by, both of the Liverpool Tidal Institute.
DARWIN—The Tide.
DEFANT—Physical Oceanography.

CHAPTER SEVEN

Tidal streams

THE VERTICAL movements of the waters encircling the globe are necessarily accompanied by the horizontal streams required to build up the dynamic gradients of the sea surface, set up by the tractive forces.

It has been shown that if a rectangular gulf of uniform depth, closed at one end, has a length equal to half the wavelength of a progressive external oceanic wave, or equal to $4.1 \text{ T } \sqrt{\text{Depth in fathoms}}$ (T = period in *hours*), a synchronous oscillation would occur about a node half-way up the gulf (Figs. III, 14-15). High Water at the entrance would occur at the same time as low water at the head of the gulf. In theory no streams would exist at the entrance, kinetic energy alone being transmitted to maintain the internal oscillation, but maximum *streams* would occur at the nodal section at the time of mean tide level. The flood stream at the node would occur as the ocean levels were falling and vice versa.

Such a gulf or long inlet of uniform width and depth is not to be found in nature, but it is *very roughly* approximated in the English Channel assuming a barrier at the Straits of Dover. Assuming also a semi-diurnal period of 12 hours and a mean depth of 36 fathoms, the formula $L = 4.1 \text{ T } \sqrt{D}$ gives a length of 300 miles for a uni-nodal system, which is roughly correct. Maximum tidal streams, accentuated by the constriction of the Cherbourg peninsula, are evident near the nodal area off the Isle of Wight as indicated by the Cotidal Chart (Fig. III, 12).

High water at the entrance synchronizes with low water near Dover, and vice-versa, in general accord with the theory under discussion.

If, on the other hand, the length of the gulf or inlet is *less than one-quarter of the length of the external oceanic undulation* and approximates 2 T $\sqrt{D}$, resonance will result, both the high and low waters inside the gulf occurring at about the *same* time as those at the entrance due to the icean or external sea. The amplitudes at the head of the gulf in this case would in theory be greater than at the entrance and this would be increased if the gulf had converging sides (Fig. III, 15). In nature friction would modify these results but they are valuable in indicating *tendencies* and often show close agreement with observation.

In the case of simple gulfs and straits of general longitudinal aspect, the streams we have been considering would alternately run in almost opposite directions, such being called *rectilinear* streams. In small streams and gulfs the stream directions are in phase with the vertical tidal movements. That is to say that the ebb and flood streams occur respectively with fall and rise. In the wider approach channels, straits and estuaries and the ocean, this is not invariably the case for a number of reasons.

DIRECTION OF TRACTIVE FORCES

In the deep oceans, where friction due to the configuration of the bottom may be disregarded, it is clear that streams will be more or less directly generated by the tractive forces and their momentum will not be sufficient to produce an appreciable gyroscopic deflection.

It can be shown by spherical trigonometry that in Latitude 30°N., magnitude and direction of the tractive force exerted by the moon in declination 15°N. would vary as shown in Fig. VII, 1.

The movement is generally clockwise and is composed of diurnal and semi-diurnal forces. It may further be demonstrated that the north and east components of the *total tractive force* vary with the semi-diurnal and diurnal forces, considered separately to produce the following rotatory effects:

(i) The direction of the semi-diurnal tractive force rotates in azimuth in a clockwise manner in the northern hemisphere and in anti-clockwise in the southern hemisphere.

The direction of the diurnal tractive force alters as the parallels of 45° N. and S. latitude and the equator are crossed and also when the moon's declination changes in sign.

For example, in north latitude when declination is positive

(or N) *diurnal* tractive forces will alter hourly in azimuth as
follows:

Latitude above 45°N.—clockwise.

Latitude 0°-45°N.—anti-clockwise.

Latitude 0°-45°S.—clockwise.

Latitude above 45°S.—anti-clockwise.

In the Atlantic Ocean where the *semi-diurnal* constituents
predominate, the simple rule of clockwise in north latitude and
vice versa is easy to remember (see Fig. III, 10).

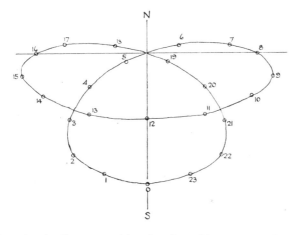

Fig. VII, I Graphically computed hourly values of lunar tractive force for Lat.
30°N., Dec. 15°N. (A.M.T.)

GYROSCOPIC EFFECT OR CORIOLIS FORCE

It has been shown in Chapter III that a particle in motion
tends to be deflected to the right in the northern hemisphere and
to the left in the southern.

Consequently, in the northern hemisphere, a rectilinear E./W.
stream of appreciable velocity would develop a south component
when running to the east and a north component when running
to the west, with the result that it would rotate 360° in clockwise
direction throughout the tidal cycle, and if magnitudes and
directions were plotted hourly the line joining them would
describe an ellipse the major axis being parallel to directions of

the maxima of the primary stream, the minor being in the meridian and a measure of the gyroscopic deflection.

Where the tidal phenomena are *semi-diurnal* it is to be observed that the tractive forces, as well as gyroscopic effects, combine to produce clockwise rotatory streams in the northern hemisphere and anti-clockwise in the southern hemisphere *so long as* single wave systems alone are considered, uncomplicated by hydraulic effects caused by uneven configuration of the sea bottom or other hydrographic features.

COMBINATION OF OSCILLATIONS OR WAVE SYSTEMS

We have seen on page 83 how two standing oscillations, one primary and the other due to gyroscopic effect, will cause an *amphidromic system* and consequently generate rotatory streams in a simple basin. In a rectangular or elongated basin the simplest combination of oscillations giving rotatory streams will be two *standing oscillations* at right angles to each other, one being *a quarter period* behind the other.

If a progressive wave along a coast crosses a standing oscillation at right-angles to the coast and the progressive wave synchronizes with high water of the standing oscillation, conditions will occur for rotatory streams that may be either clockwise *or* anti-clockwise, *depending upon the major oscillation* and the time differences between the oscillations.

EFFECT OF HYDROGRAPHIC CONTOURS

In addition to causes connected with astronomical forces and the earth's rotation, the configuration of the bottom and shape of the sea-coast, and its inlets, not only determine the incidence of combined oscillations of differing periods and amplitudes, but also cause rotatory and irregular streams through factors related properly to the principles of simple hydraulic flow.

An estuary or gulf with shelving coasts and inlets or bights will on the flood tide have transverse compensatory streams supplying the marginal areas and inlets as well as the main stream as shown in Fig. VII, 2. On the north coast the flood stream starts after hour 6, flows into the inlet at maximum rate at hour 9, terminating near hour 12 at H.W. with the main

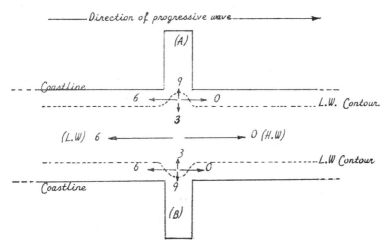

Fig. VII, 2   Streams on shelving coasts

stream.   On the ebb the stream will run out of the gulf at maximum rate at hour 3 terminating with the mean ebb at hour 6. The result at a position between the axis and the entrance to the inlet will thus be rotatory streams, clockwise in direction off the entrance to the north inlet (A) and anti-clockwise in direction off the entrance to the south inlet (B).

If, however, there are contours and governing bottom contours training the streams at different levels during rise or fall of tide, complex variations in direction will occur.   Fig. VII, 3 shows the tidal streams at the entrance to Southampton Water at the position of Calshot Light Vessel.   Here we have a number of factors causing a rotatory stream altering in a counter-clockwise direction.

As previously mentioned on page 95 the Solent stream is dominated by the difference of level between the Spithead and Needles ends respectively as shown in Fig. III, 26.

On the rise, the stream is trained by the approach channel contours (to the westward of the Light Vessel) and runs into Southampton Water in a N.N.E. direction.   As the level rises the stream flows through the North Channel and settles more and more through a N. and N.N.W. direction into the alignment of Southampton Water.   About two hours before the nearly

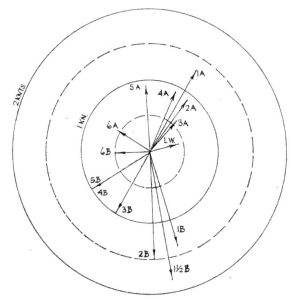

Fig. VII, 3   Magnitude and direction of tidal streams at Calshot Spit—Southampton Water (1952)

simultaneous high water at Calshot and Southampton the east-going Solent stream turns with little slack and soon runs hard to the westward, although vertical levels are still rising until the time of local high water.

After high water the tidal stream *in Southampton Water*, which is in phase with the vertical movement at and above Calshot, begins to flow out increasingly swiftly, parallel to the axis of Southampton Water in a S.E. to S.S.E. direction, until near low water when the east-going Solent stream again dominates. The result is a stream determined by several changing factors and rotating in an anti-clockwise direction.

HYDRAULIC EFFECTS

The Solent streams exemplify a periodic alteration of flow due to changing levels at each end of a long channel between Portsmouth and Needles which can be observed on a much larger scale in many other parts of the world. Streams in the axes of such channels will be rectilinear, although those inside their margins and inlets may, of course, be rotary.

One of the most outstanding examples is Seymour Narrows between Vancouver Island and the mainland near its northern end, a strait carrying heavy local coastal traffic and also situated on the United States routes to Alaska.

Here the tidal stream approaches a maximum of 8-10 knots, rendering navigation impracticable at times. This rapid stream is due to a five-hour difference in the times of high water off the north and south entrances to the narrows, high water at the north entrance occurring at the same time as low water at the southern. This produces an average alternate "head" of 13 feet which accounts for the swift stream.

Another curious case arising from a rather different cause occurs in the Gut of Canso separating Nova Scotia from Cape Breton Island. The range at both ends is about $4\frac{1}{2}$ feet and at the northern end the tide is *declinational with diurnal inequality highly developed.* (Constituents for West Point are: $M_2 + S_2 = 1.25$ feet, $K_1 + O_1 = 1.55$ feet). One daily tide may resolve itself into prolonged stand of 10-12 hours duration. At the south end the tide is of the semi-diurnal, synodic or phase type with lesser inequality. (Constituents for Cape Bear are : $M_2 + S_2 = 1.9$ feet, $K_1 + O_1 = 1.3$ feet).

The situation is further complicated by the difference in the times of high water, but the Tidal Survey of Canada has found it possible to predict the streams with fair accuracy by relating their fluctuations to the lunar declination.

It is clear that rotatory streams will be the resultant of the several complex causes which may be recapitulated as:
(a) Varying direction of the tractive forces.
(b) Gyroscopic effect due to the earth's rotation.
(c) Combination of two oscillations or wave systems.
(d) Effects of hydrographic contours, shelving coasts and training of streams at different tidal levels.

(e) Hydraulic effects of differing tidal systems at ends of straits, sounds or similar unobstructed channels open to the deeper sea at each extremity.

VARIATIONS AND DISCONTINUITIES IN FLOW

Within the continental shelves where tidal streams increase above 1 knot, oceanographers and hydrographers have—despite the considerable difficulties of tautly mooring their research craft—arrived at some general conclusions about the relation of surface to sub-surface and near-bottom velocities down to a depth of 50 fathoms (1952).

It will be seen from Fig. VII, 4 that in a depth of 50 fathoms in open water, maximum velocity occurs about 3 fathoms below the surface, thence decreasing slowly as the bottom is approached.

It is also known that obstructions on the bottom and changes in depth cause variations in the rate, and sometimes in the direction of the stream.

Coming into shoaler water, we have already noticed that as a wave travels up an estuary the crest travels faster than the base causing the ebb to have longer duration than the flood, or in other words making profile of the "up-river" side of the wave steeper than its rear.

It can be mathematically demonstrated that the relation of *elevation to width* in a converging channel is given by the following formula derived from Bernoulli's theorem:

$$\frac{\text{Change in level}}{\text{Change in width}} = \frac{C^2}{gb\left[1 - \dfrac{C^2}{gh}\right]}$$

Where b = mean width of area affected.

h = mean depth of area affected in feet

C = mean velocity of current in f.p.s.

Here the value of $\sqrt{gh}$ crops up again and we note that *as the width of the estuary decreases* the elevation.

rises if C^2 is *greater* than gh.

falls if C^2 is less than gh.

Plate I   Watts Current Meter

Acknowledgements to Liverpool University Tidal Institute

Plate II   Tide Predicting Machine

Acknowledgements to Bristol Evening Post

Plate III   River Severn Bore at Minsterworth

Acknowledgements to Mr. Potter of Trent River Board

Plate IV   River Trent Eagre or Bore—at Morton Corner

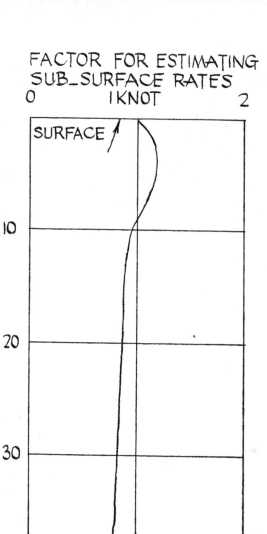

FACTOR FOR ESTIMATING
SUB_SURFACE RATES

Fig. VII, 4   General relation of surface to sub-surface streams

As $\sqrt{gh}$ is the rate of propagation of a progressive wave using the formula $C = 8.25 \sqrt{D}$ where C = knots speed ($\sqrt{gh}$)

$\qquad\qquad\qquad\qquad\qquad$ D = depth in fathoms

the following generalizations result:

Where *width* or *depth decrease* discontinuously with the progression of the current:

(a) Where speed is *greater* than C the level will *rise*.

(b) Where speed is *less* than C the level will *fall*.

Summarizing:

(i) Where width and depth decrease in the direction of the current:

$\qquad$(a) If speed is greater than C levels will rise and rate *will diminish*.

$\qquad$(c) If speed is less than C levels will fall and rate *will increase*.

(ii) Where width is unchanged and depth alone reduced in the direction of the current:

$\qquad$(a) If speed is greater than C levels will rise and rate will diminish.

$\qquad$(b) If speed is less than C, levels will fall and rate will increase.

From these conclusions we see that discontinuous constrictions of width or depth have the same effect on levels depending upon

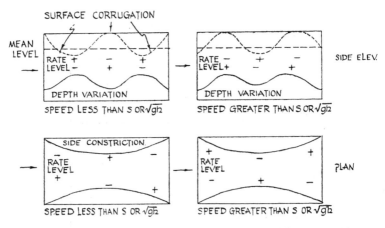

Fig. VII, 5 Effect of speed of flow in channels and effect of bottom or side constriction on surface levels.

whether the speed of the current is greater or less than C, the speed proper to free wave propagation.

As, in general, tidal stream rates are *less than* C, the bottom section will be reflected in an inverted surface profile as shown in Fig. VII, 5.   Convex shoal features on the bottom will produce concave surface profiles accompanying increased velocity.

BIBLIOGRAPHY

The Admiralty Tide Tables.
SHANKLAND, CAPTAIN E. C., R.D., R.N.R., papers by, Dock and Harbour Authority, April and May 1941.
DR. DOODSON, F.R.S.   Admiralty Manual of Tides.

CHAPTER EIGHT

Tides and the surveyor

SINCE THE fifteenth century the maritime peoples of the West have made untiring efforts to chart and record their experience of the shores of the world, but it has been the proud privilege of the Royal Navy of Britain to follow in the steps of the redoubtable Cook in reducing hydrography to a science. Since the eighteenth century the accurate survey of coasts, estuaries, and harbours has necessitated the use of a soundly estimated low water datum of soundings, generally the local level at or near mean low water springs. The seaman has from ancient times required a chart showing soundings approximately at the lowest tidal level likely to be experienced.

The old surveyors in the days of exploration always made it a practice to anchor off bays and estuaries requiring survey and send advance parties ashore, not only for trigonometric and topographical survey, but also to gain a general and preliminary estimate of tidal behaviour. When the tidal regime was roughly sized up, a survey party entered the area in small craft, on the "middle or last of the flood," when the tide was still rising; dangers could then be seen, channels discerned and their reaches related to good transits and leading marks. Dangers and channel margins were buoyed as the ship proceeded inwards on her journey of exploration and if she grounded she soon floated off, buoying the dangerous shoal features as she did so. When she put about to return, the tide had risen considerably and dangers and channel margins were safely buoyed in readiness for her outward journey, before levels began to fall on the ebb.

Throughout the last century and up to our own times, records of precise observations of tidal levels, for the purpose of reducing navigational surveys, have constituted the material from which tidal research has grown. Detailed tidal information is an essential feature of British Admiralty and other hydrographic charts and sailing directions covering all navigable areas in the world.

In addition to the observations of tidal levels, the directions and rates of tidal streams have been determined at many thousands of stations and the results are seen in the lettered or numbered tidal compartments shown on Admiralty charts. The Tidal Branch of the British Admiralty is responsible for collating and preparing details of tidal predictions and data for all parts of the world and promulgating these in many invaluable publications. The documentation for world tides possessed by this Department is the best in existence.

Tidal streams are observed in a variety of ways by the Surveyor. The old seamen of a century or so ago were satisfied with surface rates determined by a wooden 120° segment, weighted at its arc perimeter barely to float and known as a "log-ship." It was secured to a calibrated line and launched from a ship anchored in the tideway. The amount of line run out, timed over a sand-glass interval, enabled the speed of the surface current to be determined.

Since these early days the maximum draught of ships has increased to over 50 feet and it has, therefore, become necessary to ascertain average rates at mean depths of 15-25 feet from the surface. To achieve this, the hydrographic surveyor generally uses a 35 foot spar of uniform square cross-section, weighted for the immersion of, say, 30 feet of its entire length.

This may be used with a calibrated line and stop-watch timing from an anchored vessel, and rates and directions determined at quarter—or half-hourly intervals. This method is the one most generally used, but there are difficulties if depths are considerable and the ship cannot be tautly moored with two anchors. Unless this is done, small movements of the ship are included in the observations and the measurements of small rates below half a knot may be quite erroneous. Above this rate, unless the ship is seriously wind-rode, and sheering, rates can be recorded with sufficient accuracy for the purpose of safe navigation.

Many mechanical devices have been designed to enable currents to be measured at specific depths, and whilst they have given excellent results in river gauging and shoal water, it is generally true to say that no fully satisfactory mechanical instrument has yet been devised for *general* nautical survey. The majority of the devices work on the principle of a propeller of suitable pitch oriented by a fin which keeps the axis parallel to the stream. The movement of the propeller is communicated to a simple clockwork recording mechanism. The instrument is lowered to the required depth on a wire secured to a point above the centre of gravity of the instrument. See Plate X.

A significant advance in instrumentation has however been achieved in the design of the Direct Reading Current Meter made by Messrs. Kelvin Hughes (Marine) Limited and designed by Mr. A. J. Woods of their Research Division.

By this instrument rates of flow and direction at intervals of say 10 feet below waterline can be read off directly and immediately on a dial in the survey ship.

The order of accuracy achieved is as follows:—

(a) Velocity to within 0.1 knot.

(b) Direction to within 2°.

The accuracy for direction has not been possible on any previously devised instrument and represents a great step forward. The author collaborated in trials of this meter at Southampton in 1959 and results are given in Appendix II.

Instruments have now been designed for lowering to the bottom and recording bottom currents with some precision and it would seem that this solution is the most promising for shallow-water observations. Buoyant current meters can then be released from sinkers to the requisite levels and observations made over long periods, using clock mechanisms for recording. Such a device would give scope for methods employing a magnetic compass for directional recording which obviously cannot be used from iron vessels.

The above expedients for observing tidal streams might be called static methods, as observations are taken from fixed sites, i.e. jetties, buoys, or moored and anchored ships.

Excellent results are, however, obtained by drift-float methods involving the "following up" of floats or spars so designed as to represent the action of the tidal stream at special depths or to give an average value over a certain range of depth, say, from the surface down to 30 feet. An attendant launch closes with the float at frequent stop-watch intervals and fixes position by double simultaneous sextant angles taken on triangulated shore objects.

When the series is plotted, direction and rate can be calculated for any part of the run and results are very representative of the effect of the tidal stream on ships whose draughts equal that of the immersed length of the spar. The difficulty involved in using this method over areas of uneven depth is that the spar may ground during the run. If, however, the hydrographic contours and depths have previously been determined, it is easy for an attendant launch equipped with echo sounding to launch a shorter spar at the right time in anticipation, recover the deeper spar and use it again when the depth increases.

Several types of float or "logship" have been used to investigate flow at depths intermediate between the surface and the bottom levels. As stated above, the vertical spar gives very good results for the mean rate at depths of half the immersed length below the surface.

If, however, it is required to determine the direction and rate at specific depths the free box float is a simple but most valuable device which is capable of giving very accurate and practical results. This is similar in construction to a box kite and consists of a wooden frame about 4 feet 6 inches long covered by canvas and open at its upper and lower ends as shown in Fig. VIII, 1. It is weighted to give a slight negative buoyancy, after complete soaking, and is suspended by a fine non-resistant wire to a small wooden mark float coupling adequate buoyancy with small surface and wind resistance. The "Iroquois" free float or "log-ship" is a similar device using four canvas vanes instead of the "box." The devices are set with a wire scope to keep the centre of lateral resistance at the required depth, released and followed up by a survey launch which closes with the float at stop-watch intervals for observations, the track being recorded by simultaneous double-angle resections within a good system of shore control. Care has to be taken that the float does not ground or foul, and, as in the case of the spar log-ship, a substitute of lesser draught must be held in readiness and dropped alongside the original float in anticipation of shoaler bottom features.

These free logship devices have proved invaluable for the investigation of the direction and rate of dominant bottom scouring

FREE FLOATS

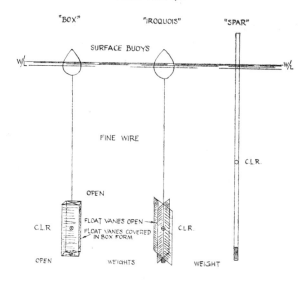

Fig. VIII, I   Various free float devices for measuring tidal streams

flow in estuaries as a preliminary to setting out economic dredged channels.

The rectification of the Yanlet Channel in the Thames was effected in this manner for the Port of London Authority by Captain E. C. Shankland, R.D., R.N.R., who informed the writer that such bottom floats were quite successful and that dredging costs were greatly reduced by rectification of the dredged bottom cut along the lines indicated by the observations. The writer was able to apply similar methods in Southampton Water thereby reducing maintenance dredging at one particular site by over 60%.

In Appendix II details of the recently devised Direct Reading Current Meter are given and it would appear that this instrument is a great advance on methods used hitherto.

TIDAL DATUMS

Hydrographic surveyors, in producing charts for navigators, are governed in their methods of presentation by sound canons of navigation evolved throughout centuries of painful experience. Consequently, it may be taken as a general principle that sea charts show soundings reduced to a low water level *"so low that the tide will but seldom fall below it"* which was as near as the International Hydrographic Conference of 1926 was able to get to a definition. The reason for this is, of course, that the navigator must not, in the normal course of his approaches to land, be required to subtract from the soundings shown on his vital documents, but on the contrary should rather be assured that such depths are almost the shallowest definitions of the underwater features represented.

Such hydrographic datums may be regarded as planes only in a most restricted and local sense and are in fact "utility" levels plotted below Mean Sea Level and varying sometimes by several feet over very short distances on account of hydraulic features. Over an extended coastal area, *where tides are semi-diurnal* such a datum line would in fact, be plotted as a curve with abscissae for distance in miles and ordinates in feet plotted below Mean Sea Level for values of about 1.2 (height of M_2 + height of S_2), such being a slightly lower level than Mean Low Water springs, in semi-diurnal areas.

The work of the cartographer in combining the hydrographic levels of several local surveys in one document will roughly consist in reducing soundings to such a "utility" curve of levels for the benefit of the judicious navigator requiring *governing least depths*. The French hydrographic datum, is regarded with characteristic Gallican logic, as the lowest possible low water and whilst undoubtedly safe it describes a situation which occurs at relatively rare intervals. This is regarded as an unnecessary inhibition by Anglo-Saxon seamen. On the east coast of the United States, where ranges are not usually large, the plane of Mean Low Water springs given by M.S.L. $-$ (H of M_2 + H of S_2)—is used. Where the diurnal tide is large, that is where $K_1 + O_1 > 2 M_2$, it is usual to establish a datum by experience rather lower than (M.S.L. $-$ ($M_2 + S_2 + K_1 + O_1$)) which was the formula suggested for Indian Spring low water, but below which diurnal tides can *somtimes fall at springs*, due to other factors. Indirectly, therefore, the tidal semi-range must be referred to the more stable Mean Sea Level, which is truly a plane and is approximated in most land survey datums of civilized nations and projected along the land surfaces by precise levelling.

If no astronomical, meteorological and seismic disturbing forces existed, the sea surfaces of our planet would adjust themselves to planes normal to the plumb-line and attain an ideal Mean Sea Level for the geoid. When one considers the purely astronomical tractive forces, there are long-period constituents within the solar year, viz. Sa and Ssa, which must also be considered in close analysis for M.S.L.

Furthermore, longer periods which are approximately multiples of the Metonic (19-year) cycle, have been inferred from observations and it is thought that these may be due to changes in the lunar orbit. Again for reasons as yet unaccountable, the Mean Sea Level on the British coasts rises slightly from south to north on all coasts and is 10 inches higher at Dunbar than at Newlyn in Cornwall.

It is remarkable that the fundamental and initial level for the "Liverpool" system of bench marks for Great Britain established by 1860 was based on a M.S.L. determination deduced from only one week's observations at the port of Liverpool. Apart from the fact that shallow water effects were included and gave Mean Tide Level, the seasonal and meteorological effects were not considered and the resultant plane could only be regarded as a very approximate representation of Mean Sea Level.

The second levelling, begun in 1912, is based on a value determined by six years' continuous records at Newlyn, Cornwall, and this plane has been extended by very high precision levelling which in one isolated case varied from the first levelling by as much as 1.8 feet.

So far as meteorological changes in M.S.L. are concerned these are partly irregular, but some are distinctly regular over an annual period, and are tabulated in the Admiralty Tide Tables.

In areas liable to seismic activity it is necessary to resort to tidal observations for redefinition of M.S.L. after disturbances in shore levels. Clearly no other method is possible and where, as in the case of New Zealand, a big earthquake takes place, observations free from serious shallow water effects must be taken to redetermine temporary M.S.L. values for shore engineering reference levels, also safe low water datums of soundings for hydrographic surveys of harbour approaches after seismic activity has subsided.

The sea surface is the only plane of reference in such circumstances, and it is important that the land plane of reference should *not* be determined by observations in harbours where changes in submarine levels have accentuated shallow water effect and consequently give a new mean *tide* level.

A table in the *Admiralty Manual of Tides*, page 111, using multipliers for thirty-eight continuous observations, is probably the best method for obtaining a good value for M.S.L. quickly, and this can be repeated at intervals to cover seasonal and meteorological variations (Appendix III).

At terminal ports and all places where engineering works are contemplated, it is of the highest importance that the precise behaviour of tidal levels should be known to enable the engineer to superimpose accurately the build-up due to storm conditions and above which he must securely plan his foundations, or wharf levels.

Tables for levels between high and low waters for all ranges of tide can be computed with fair accuracy as described on page 107 and shown by Table I, but it is very necessary to determine the possibility of the *highest possible* astronomical tide being increased by meteorological activity. An appeal to the oldest inhabitant may, or may not, elicit a soundly witnessed historical level to which a tide has attained under gale conditions, and the writer can remember a statement that "the spring tide comes right up to my garden fence at neaps."

In Atlantic areas where synodical or semi-diurnal tides prevail, it is reasonable to consider $1.2 (M_2 + S_2 + K_1 + O_1)$, as a maximum rise of the astronomical tide above Mean Sea Level and to add an increment for the *maximum possible rise* in estuaries or harbour areas where there is little windward "fetch," or there is interrupted sea to windward. Careful determination of this increment by historical research is essential.

If, on the other hand, roads or permanent ways or embankments are being constructed on a lee shore and on an exposed coast, secure, of course, from erosive possibilities, one should add to astronomical highest possible high water ($+ x$ feet) a proportion of the wave height deduced from Stevenson's formula $H = 1.5 \sqrt{d}$, where H is a maximum possible value.*

Where H = wave height in feet.

d = uninterrupted windward sea distance or "fetch" in nautical miles (up to 900 miles, above which there is no increase in height).

(See Chapter X under "Meteorological Surges").

It is important in this connection to know the prevalence of the strongest gales likely to develop along the axis of greatest fetch or whether the area is liable to cyclonic disturbances.

Where the tides are diurnal it is generally true that ranges are relatively small, but the determination of highest possible astronomical high water cannot be made by means of the four basic harmonic constants, and should be determined from close analysis and prediction for maximum values at an authoritative tidal institute. Such authorities as the Liverpool Tidal Institute should be consulted for maximum storm surge increments.

---

* A correlation of the sources of oceanography and isostasy show a greater variation in sea level than was hitherto suspected and authorities should be consulted for consideration of this long term increment for design levels at any given locality. For the South coast of England a value of nearly 1 foot rise of Mean Sea Level per century has been mentioned and would be a prudent figure to accept in design.

BIBLIOGRAPHY

Any standard work on Hydrographic Surveying.
SHANKLAND, CDR. E. C., R.N.R.—Modern Harbours (James Brown, 1926).
Papers in Dock and Harbour Authority, for April and May, 1941.

CHAPTER NINE

Tidal factors in history, commerce and sea power

IT HAS been shown in Chapter I that the British Islands were, in ancient times, an Ultima Thule for those hardy venturers who were prepared to acquire a sound knowledge of the tidal ranges and streams off the British and French coasts as a necessary passport to the mineral riches they were seeking. The Phoenician-Hebrew traders with the early Britons did not disclose their tidal lore to such Mediterranean rivals as the Romans for obvious reasons. Ports and estuaries which "dried out" at low water, presented a confusing aspect to seamen unaccustomed to tidal foreshores with small gradients and the disasters accompanying the first invasion of Britain by Caesar are significant witnesses to Roman ignorance in this respect.

Bores and tide rips and the phenomena of periodic short confused seas, caused by strong winds adverse in direction to tidal streams, would not commend themselves, even to the Spanish seamen at the time of the Armada. Then, the ships of Drake were often able to withdraw to safe vantage points in the lee of weather shores and dangers, to recoup and repair sails and rigging whilst their assailants used all their energies in giving wide berths to the land and outlying shoals, handling their gear with hazard and driving to leeward withal.

Summing up these facts, it is not difficult to see how the schooling of the tides has formed an aptitude for the vagaries of the sea in the mind and philosophy of the peoples of the British Isles, and thus contributed to their ascendancy and the influence of their sea-power in history.

It is generally characteristic of the great and ancient ports of the world that they are situated at the mouths of large rivers. London, Liverpool, Hamburg, Antwerp, Bordeaux are all examples of this in the old world, and New York and San Francisco in the new. Southampton Water is a remarkable exception as the three rivers, Hamble, Test and Itchen, have relatively small discharges, the natural features being due to relatively recent subsidence.

The tidal regime at the mouth of a river with normal bed slope leading to the sea is an invaluable link with the higher reaches at high water times. In mediaeval times, Cologne was one of the great Hanseatic ports offering a 6 foot channel approach extending 120 miles up the Rhine.

Modern ports are frequently 50-70 miles above the mouth, locking and docking being possible only at high water times. London, Liverpool, and Cardiff, for example, have Mean Spring ranges of 21¼, 27 and 37 feet respectively, which approach the economic load draughts of large modern cargo ships approximating 30 feet.

The advance and relative precision of steam navigation, in the nineteenth century, the larger quantities of cargoes carried and consequently greater draughts of ships, necessitated either the deepening of these estuaries and ports possessing natural advantages and manageable tidal streams, or, where large ranges prevail, the development of locking systems which can accept the deeper draught ships at times near high water on the tidal lift and lock them into watertight basins and systems involving reasonable maintenance costs.

NATURAL ESTUARIES AND HARBOURS

Those natural estuaries exemplified by Southampton Water, New York Harbour and the other American ports, where the average or mean spring tidal range is *less than* 15 *feet*, are examples of the former type of terminal where maintenance by dredging is economically viable. In such terminals the rise and fall can be met by engineering design at docks and adequate crane, gantry, and mooring adjustments.

Where the tidal streams, being functions of tidal range, are not unduly large, reasonably slack water intervals for berthing are consequently available; also the absence of heavy scouring on the geological base has generally kept these estuaries free of large quantities of sand and thus immune from the variable bars and shifting shoals which accompany this material.

Furthermore, rapid siltage of approach channels, providing they are suitably aligned to dominant tidal flow, is much less probable in such tidal regimes. If the estuary or harbour is due to relatively recent geological subsidence—as in the case of Southampton (10,000-5,000 B.C.)—the clay base is ideal for the economic cutting of stable sea channels.

Incidentally, the Clyde (range about 10 feet) was at one time a small stream fordable in summer 12 miles below Glasgow.

LOCKING HARBOURS AND PORTS

Where the tidal range exceeds a value of about 15 feet, tidal velocities generally limit berthing very strictly to the times near high water and have, over long geological eras, with weathering, produced immense quantities of transportable sandy or silty material and detritus in the approaches. Consequently the cost of maintaining such approach channels becomes prohibitive if levels other than those near high water are considered for access by the larger vessels.

The large rise and fall precludes the berthing and discharge of ships lying alongside tidal quays without involving insuperable obstacles to design and economic maintenance. Where a range of over 15 feet exists, recourse must be had to extensive locking systems, which can accept the deep draught ship or lock her outwards near high water times, when tidal streams are nearly slack and safe manoeuvring is possible.

Usually the two major limitations of those ports requiring locking systems are time restriction and length of channel access respectively, taken with the financial and conservancy problems raised by both aspects, particularly the latter which involves heavy responsibility in channel marking.

The suitability of New York and Southampton as terminals for the closely scheduled largest and fastest liners in the world, drawing 40 feet, is determined by their tidal ranges which are below the 15 foot limit, with the accompanying features outlined above that follow from this fact in all such natural estuaries. Super-tankers drawing up to 50 feet and displacing 100,000 tons are now accepted at Southampton.

In both cases, access to open quays and jetties is possible through relatively short and direct approach channels, capable of economic maintenance and at arrival times compatible with reasonable scheduling and speed adjustments between terminals.

Furthermore, for reasons given above, large ships are not obliged to await berthing at anchor between high water times, with relatively poor holding ground accompanied by strong tidal streams—features which generally occur together.

Another valuable function of tidal flow in estuaries situated near areas subject to ice formation in the winter time, is to keep such harbours open by introducing salt water on the flood tide period and thus lowering freezing-point. For example, New York, on the Lower Hudson, is open throughout the winter, whilst the Upper Hudson is ice-bround.

The treatment of the large quantities of sewage discharged near modern, densely populated sea terminals situated at the heads of estuaries or on rivers, by successive floodings of fresh salt water is of incalculable value. Without tidal movement around the ports of London and Liverpool, for example the safe disposal of sewage would constitute a formidable engineering problem.

Indeed, it is interesting to speculate upon the path history would have taken if the British Islands had been surrounded by a tideless sea. The segregation of hardy peoples in migration to our islands for centuries and the acquiring of distinctive qualities in the mastery of tidal phenomena, constituting a world force in sea power, would not have come, and the whole of the West would probably have been assimilated to Mediterranean civilization without any insuperable natural barriers apart from periodic bad weather. The absence of tidal floodings up the long entrance reaches of our rivers would have limited the draughts of ships capable of connecting their voyages with natural land termini, and the modern revolution in steam navigation would have demanded deeper dredging over long channel reaches, for access to ports such as Bristol, Liverpool, or London. Such in all probability would not have occurred.

Furthermore, the sea reaches we now use would be mere river beds, unexcavated by the semi-diurnal scourings which over incalculable periods have so eroded their sections as to

Plate IVa   River Trent Eagre—at Gainsborough

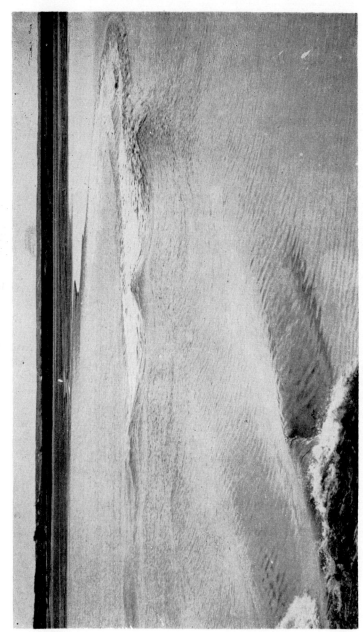

Plate V   Tidal Bore coming in—Moncton New Brunswick

anticipate our basic modern requirements.   Our locking systems, with the high lifts now possible by utilizing tidal rise, would be pointless, and the deep dredging of entire approaches and basins would be a costly matter.

Again, let us consider the removal of the tidal obstacle to the modern invasion of Britain.

It is fortunate that the tidal range at Dover, the nearest point to the continent of Europe, is considerable and that the planning of an invasion in either direction must narrowly consider tidal factors.   There is little doubt that the war staffs of powers planning the destruction of the womb of seapower and freedom have found the tidal regime around the British coasts to be a formidable obstacle to their designs.   It is, therefore, reasonable to assume that the influence of the tides on world history is not inconsiderable, and that a fortuitous combination of large tidal ranges and rich mineral resources in the British Islands has, despite changing aspects, determined the character, course and ascendancy of the Anglo-Saxon peoples and the expansion of their free institutions and cultures.

BIBLIOGRAPHY

MARMER—The Tide.
BREASTED—Ancient Times (1944).
FROUDE—English Seamen of the Sixteenth Century.

K

CHAPTER TEN

Tidal Miscellany

IT MUST not be imagined that the application of modern scientific methods of analysis has eliminated all the question marks or elucidated all the mysteries connected with the study of tidal phenomena. It may however be said that existing discrepancies between theory and the observed tides are generally due to the lack of quantitative data in those regions of research where apparent anomalies or inconsistencies prevail.

It is characteristic of our transition from the Victorian to the modern era that we now use dynamical hypotheses as the keys which are the most likely to open the newer windows upon the natural universe, and its expanding horizons.

SHALLOW WATER TIDES

In tidal science the correspondence of the energy equations in natural hydraulic movement with simple and complex harmonic motion has justified the method of harmonic analysis for tidal motion and opened the way to rapid numerical analysis and prediction. Nevertheless precise agreement between observed and predicted curves in localities where shallow-water effects are considerable, as in the case of Southampton, have not yet been achieved. Whilst the introduction of the sixth diurnal constituent wave gives an approximation to the observed curve in Southampton it would be necessary to introduce a great number of the higher species of shallow water tides to give closer approximations to natural facts and indeed to reveal the double high water feature as well as the "young flood" halt.

The two entrances on either side of the Isle of Wight, their differing tidal ranges and sections and their distance apart introduce hydraulic factors of considerable complexity. The hydraulic factors involved in the alternating east-west flow in the Solent due to varying range "head", cause that peculiar perturbation of the M_2 tide that here reverses the normal phase relationship with the MS_4 tide and brings about the valuable and unusual longer flood tide period of 6¾ hours as compared with an ebb period of only 3¾ hours. A hydraulic model of this area with suitable vertical and horizontal scale relationships has contributed to our knowledge of the causes of this fortuitous interference with the semi-diurnal tide in the offing. Yet allowing for all these difficulties it is still true that the tidal scientist can always make predictions within the accuracy required for careful navigation on his basic assumption that "the characteristic variations of the equilibrium tide exhibit the characteristic variations of the existing tide in greater or less degree " and that harmonic analysis will enable practical estimates of the degree of response to the various astronomical disturbing cycles to be made.

OCEANIC TIDES

It is still true to say that it is impossible to define with any precision the co-tidal lines for any ocean. This is largely due to the insuperable difficulties still connected with the close measurement of the small oceanic ranges in the deep water where they are found.

Towards the close of the nineteenth century considerable progress was made in applying the principles of stationary waves and the theory of resonance to oceanic areas by Harris, a mathematician of the United States Coast and Geodetic Survey; but quite apart from his omission to consider the interaction of the movements in each system on their boundaries, his neglect of the gyroscopic effects of the earth's rotation held up, for a time, a promising advance in our understanding of the tides in the oceans.

The fulfilment of his theories in rotary amphidromic systems represents the latest stage in our theoretical knowledge, and for some thirty years the Liverpool Tidal Institute, under the supervision of Dr. Doodson, F.R.S., has carried on intensive mathematical research and constructed systems of co-tidal lines for seas of 2,630 fathoms uniform depth and bounded by meridians 50°, 70°, 90° and 180° apart, thus ranging respectively from Atlantic to Pacific dimensions.

These calculations clearly indicate the predominance of amphidromic systems in the great oceans, but it is obvious that irregularities of boundaries, shape and depth involve such modifications in the simple shapes and uniform depths assumed that we cannot compute the results for any ocean direct from the astronomical disturbing forces without close local observation and analysis.

Although, as stated in the opening of Chapter I, the tidal ranges of the Mediterranean basin do not average more than about 1 foot, greater values do appear in the Gulf of Gabes off Tunisia and in the Northern Adriatic where the extreme ranges amount to 7 and 4 feet respectively.

It is now considered that the Eastern and Western Mediterranean oscillate independently and in the case of the eastern basin, lying to the eastward of Sicily a node exists located roughly at the western end of Crete.

The bight lying between Mahdia, north of the Gulf of Gabes and 12° East longitude appears to be in very close resonance with the total oscillation in the eastern Mediterranean basin and also being a N./S. barrier at its western extremity, the range can build up to a maximum of about 7 feet—sufficient to enable a landing craft to be careened.

The Adriatic also resonates with the major oscillation, an amphidromic point occurring off the Dalmatian Islands, lying midway between Zadar (Yugo-Slavia) and Ancona (Italy).

The Tunisian system is dominantly semi-diurnal but in the Adriatic the semi-diurnal element whilst dominant near Trieste is inferior, in the southern part of the sea, to the diurnal.

METEOROLOGICAL SURGES

It has been shown in Chapter VI that variations of atmospheric pressure and the prevalence of strong surface winds resulting from pressure gradients and their movements in synchronism with the natural periods of oscillation of oceanic areas, may build up heavy tidal surges or seiches. The arrival of such surges at the continental shelves and their modification by shallow-water features and resonating inlets and gulfs, may lead to catastrophic results.

A typical example is the disaster from this cause which occurred at Galveston, Texas on 8 September, 1850. On 6 September, the barometer which stood high, began to fall rapidly. On the next day the swell in the Gulf of Mexico began to work up and flooding began in the lower parts of Galveston. Events on the following day, 8 September, are set out in the following statement:

8 September 1500 Half the streets flooded.

1700 Wind rising to hurricane force.

1850 Wind attained 100 m.p.h. Recording apparatus blown away.

1900 Barometer 29.42. Wind attaining 120 m.p.h.

1930 Water level suddenly rose 4 feet in 15 seconds and continued to rise.

2030 Barometer 28.48. Water level rose to 15 feet above Mean High Water Level and thence began slowly to recede.

On the following day the sun arose on a scene of almost unparalleled devastation, 6,000 human beings having perished overnight.

During the year 1950 heavy gales on the eastern American seaboard caused similar phenomenal surges occasioning much widespread damage and loss of life.

SEISMIC SURGES AND SEICHES

Popular journalism is incorrigible in that it persists in regarding every spectacular surge of the seas as a "tidal wave" when, in fact, these surges are inevitably due either to meteorological or seismic disturbances. Most of the so-called "tidal waves" have been of seismic origin, the oceanic perturbations travelling as free progressive waves until they are modified by shallow water or transmit their energy to arms of the sea oscillating in resonance with their periods.

At San Francisco at the time of the Krakatoa earthquake—10,000 miles distant—in August 1883, a seiche of over 6 inches range with a 40-minute period was recorded 18-hours after the eruption. In November 1922, an earhquake on the east coast of Chile, 5,000 miles distant, caused a seiche of the same period and amplitude.

At Honolulu, where the range averages 1 foot only, a surge derived from the Krakatoa earthquake imposed a seiche of 0.7 feet range with a 20-minute period on the normal curve.

At the same place on 3 February, 1923, a seiche of 2 feet range was recorded 6 hours after the Kamchatka earthquake and persisted with slowly diminishing range for three days.

Fig. X, 0 shows a seismic surge which occurred in the Pacific in 1957 and originated in a submarine earthquake near the Aleutian Islands.

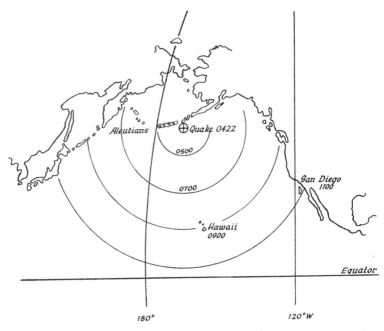

Fig. X, 0 Progress of Pacific surge originating from Aleutian quake in 1957

It remains to consider the possibilities of seiches produced by man who, by his discovery of the origins and applications of nuclear fission, has himself, for good or ill, become a cosmic force.

The recent experiments carried out by the United States Navy off the Bikini Atoll indicate the grim possibilities of large-scale wave-making by under-water nuclear explosions at optimum depths off enemy coasts.

To reduce human belligerence to its ultimate absurdity we may imagine a hostile wave-making task force creating undulations which are frustrated by introducing at the right time a train of defensive oscillations by suitable explosions!

TIDAL CYCLES IN BIOLOGY

Scientific research has recently vindicated what used to be regarded as the naive conviction of the ancients of the eastern Mediterranean, that the tides and lunar phases determined the size of sea urchins and their periods of reproduction. This tradition is today perpetuated by the fishmongers of Suez and modern research has confirmed to a remarkable degree that sea urchins (Centrechinus-Diadema-sectosus) are subject to a periodic reproduction cycle which is correlated with the lunar month. It is not clear, however, whether this phenomenon is conditioned by the periodic maxima of tidal streams—tides are semi-diurnal and of appreciable range at Suez—or by polarized light, the volume of which would be determined by the amount of illumination of the moon's disc and thus directly dependent upon the synodic cycle.

A most interesting letter in *Nature* (Vol. 130, 1932, p. 23) by Dr. Fox, who gave a paper on the subject before the Royal Society, includes the following statement:

"Recent experimental work, however, on the influence of light on sexual periodicity, suggests a way in which moonlight might impose a lunar periodicity. In mammals and birds the length of the breeding season appears to depend in part on the daily number of hours during which the animals are exposed to light. Thus the moon may perhaps cause a lunar cycle in reproduction, not through its relatively small intensity of light as compared with that of the sun but by the additional total number of hours of illumination per 24 hours at full moon *over and above* a threshold value. Only experimental work can test this hypothesis."

A most remarkable annual phenomenon occurs off the Californian coast in the tidal control of the spawning of the grunion.

This fish (Leuresthes tenuis) is a shore dweller and I am indebted to the Californian State Fisheries Laboratory for permission to use and quote freely from an illuminating paper by Frances Clark, entitled Grunion in Southern California:

"The spawning season extends from March to August and during these months the female ripens a batch of eggs at two-week intervals. Thus spawning occurs only every two weeks and the time required to mature a batch of eggs is so mysteriously adjusted that the fish are ready to spawn only on the three or four nights when occur the exceptionally high tides (springs) accompanying the full and dark of the moon.

"These spawning runs take place only at night and only on those nights when each succeeding tide is lower than on the proceeding night.

"On any given night, the run occurs just at or somewhat after the turn of the tide and lasts for about one hour. The grunion are washed up on the beach with the larger waves; the female quickly digs tail first into the sand for about half the depth of her body then extrudes her eggs which are fertilized by the male as he lies arched around her."

The whole process of laying takes only about half a minute. The eggs lying buried close to the high water level are buried deeper in the sand as the beach is built up by later but lower tides, and lie in the warm moist-sand.

A fortnight later the spring tides erode the beach, free the eggs, which immediately hatch the baby grunion, these being washed out into their natural element.

"Thus an extremely delicate adjustment between fish and tidal phenomena assures the perpetuation of a fish unique in its spawning behaviour. If the eggs did not ripen at intervals corresponding to the occurrence of the highest tides the grunion might spawn on a series of tides which increases in magnitude each tide. This would result in the eggs being dug out and washed back to the sea before hatching time had arrived. For the same reason, if the grunion spawned on any given night before the turn of the tide the eggs might also be washed out to sea. This mishap is avoided because the fish do not run up on the beach until the tide is on the ebb."

The dates and times of the "runs" are computed accurately from the predicted times of the night spring water times—about 2100 hours—and they commence about fifteen minutes after this tide has culminated.

The phenomenon always occurs on the evening tide and at both new and full moon between April and August of each year. It would seem that the grunion is controlled by the periodic hydraulic phenomena connected with variations in the tidal range and consequently in the strength of the tidal streams, but

the discrimination shown in their precise spawning operation
has yet to be explained on scientific grounds.

At San Diego, which is in this region, the tides have a mean
spring range of about 6 feet, but are of a mixed character, and
much affected by declination. By permission of the California
Fish Laboratory the relation of tides at San Diego to the grunion
runs is shown in Fig. X, 1.

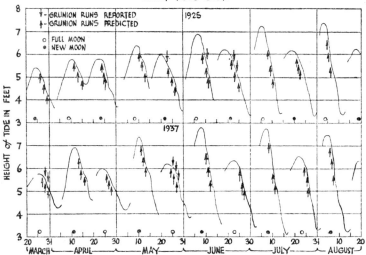

Fig. X, I Tidal conditions necessary for grunion runs at San Diego, California.
(From California State Fisheries Laboratory)

TIDAL MODELS

It is considered appropriate to make some remarks concerning
tidal models in view of the fact that the subject is receiving
increasing attention. It must, however, be stated that these are
not given for any other reason than to enable readers to gain a
general view of this interesting subject, which will probably
stimulate them to further reading in the specialist branches in
which they may be interested. It should here be said at once
that the writer is no specialist on this matter, and it is quite

possible that many of his statements may be controverted and they are, therefore, given in the light of his own experience. The Solent tidal model (hard bed) was built to his tidal specification by the University of Southampton and a brief description is given in Appendix IV.

The whole problem of model fundamentals has often proved to be an arena of strong controversy, eminent names of tidal physicists and hydraulic experts figuring on different sides. It will, therefore, be seen that the subject requires a great deal of further research before universally acceptable first principles have been agreed.

The following summary of the present state of model research by one of the most eminent experts of the day, may now perhaps be given at the outset and must be regarded as qualifying the observations of the present writer:

"Where conditions are stable, which is unusual in the sea, models constructed to suitable scales show lines of flow satisfactorily, but where bed movement is an important factor, large models are essential, and due to our knowledge about the 'movement of bed materials' being far from complete, experimentation with loose boundary models still remains *more of an art than a science*, requiring a natural flair, much experience in the field and a gift for diagnosis."

The following general remarks are given to assist readers in appreciating the problems involved in tidal models which are still matters of strong controversy, although in many countries considerable advances in theory are being achieved.

Civil engineers have, for many reasons, been obliged to study with close attention, the behaviour of rivers, and particularly those having exceptionally great and varying discharges with beds in soft and alluvial material.

One of the tools of the harbour and river engineer is the hydraulic small-scale model, but there are still many basic problems requiring solution in this technique which is very complex. Good practical results have been obtained in the prediction of the features involved in the tendencies of channel and river flow, where bed features are stable, and there have been successful forecasts of the effect of artificial works over future cycles of years.

Furthermore, by using appropriate scales, the model cycles in weeks will represent long natural cycles over periods of years, and model tendencies, when they can be correctly interpreted by an experienced specialist, will reveal to the engineer features which he can further investigate either by full-scale observation or mathematical analysis.

In the river model it has been found that *geometrical* similarity between model and river section does not give results corresponding to nature. If, however, the vertical scale is exaggerated in a certain proportion to the horizontal scale, a significant correspondence in "soft bed" contours often follows and the model reproduces natural features to a remarkable degree.

The velocity of flow is dependent on the surface slope and the alignment, also the "boundary roughness" of the particular channel. For the purpose of calculation the last mentioned (i.e. "boundary" or wetted bed surface roughness) is customarily taken account of by the term "hydraulic Radius" (R) which is defined as the cross sectional area below the hydraulic surface (A) divided by the wetted perimeter (P). Fig. X, 2.

$$\text{Thus } R = \frac{A}{P}$$

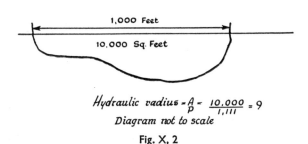

$$\text{Hydraulic radius} = \frac{A}{P} = \frac{10,000}{1,111} = 9$$

Diagram not to scale

Fig. X, 2

A convenient approximate empirical formula for calculating the rate of flow in an open natural channel fairly straight and free of boulders or rocks with an earth, alluvial or sandy bottom is given by:

$$C = \frac{\sqrt{FR}}{K}$$

Where C = Speed in knots.

F = Fall in inches per nautical mile.

R = Hydraulic radius or $\dfrac{A}{P}$

K = A constant taken from the following table:

R	1	$2\frac{1}{2}$	5	10	20	30	50	R
K	8.3	6.6	5.4	4.8	4.2	3.9	3.7	K

For example let us take a channel 1000 feet wide with an average cross sectional area of 10,000 square feet and a wetted perimeter of 1,110 feet.

$$R = \frac{A}{P} = \frac{10000}{1110} = 9 \text{ nearly}$$

From Table K = 4.9

Let us assume a surface fall in level or slope of 9 inches in 1 nautical mile $=F$

$$C = \frac{\sqrt{FR}}{4.9} = \frac{9 \times 9}{4.9} = \frac{9}{4.9} = 1.835 \text{ knots (mean velocity)}$$

This is of course an approximation and sinuosity, variation in cross sectional area and bed roughness would need to be considered for more precise estimation.

Some underlying reason for the necessary and so-called "exaggeration" in the vertical scale of small-scale river and channel models is revealed when observing the result of flow, in soft alluvium, of rivers with varying discharges to which the bed must continually adjust itself for the maintenance of equilibrium, or "regime" as it is called.

When the volume of the discharge is reduced from that of a river to a small stream, the width is also drastically reduced, whilst diminution of depth is relatively small as shown in Fig. X, 3.

Consequently, as the small-scale model is really *a stream in its own right*, with a small discharge, it may be more correct to talk about a reduction in the horizontal scale than about an exaggeration of the vertical.

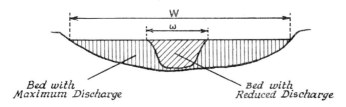

Fig. X, 3

The precise relationship between all the factors involved has been sought by many eminent engineers and physicists, but, apart from actual experience in interpreting models, there are many gaps in our knowledge of the complex ancillary factors involved. It is a remarkable fact however that when a suitable relationship between horizontal and vertical scales has been found the use of the actual grain size of silt and sand in nature gives some approximation to natural performance in the model. Of course, if the angle of repose, or slope of the bed material, is small, the exaggeration in vertical scale will prevent stabilization of slopes in the model at natural gradients; but despite this a remarkable agreement between theory and observation has often been achieved in limited spheres and has proved of the greatest value in solving conservancy problems.

The researches of Dr. Reynolds commencing in 1885 with the Mersey model which was based upon experience of river models, that had hitherto dealt only with *one-way flow*, were so spectacular as to give a tremendous and continuing impetus to the building of models of tidal estuaries, although many experts would now hesitate to draw the original conclusions.

Reynolds, who had used a horizontal scale of 1/31,800 (2,650 feet to the inch), and a vertical scale of about 1/960 (80 feet to the inch), happily struck a relation which has been generally confirmed by later research, as roughly appropriate to his experiment.

The law of dynamical similarity governing the analogy in time units of such a model is given by the following formula:

$$\frac{t}{T} = \frac{\sqrt{y}}{x}$$

Where t = model time.

T = natural time.

y = denominator of vertical scale.

x = denominator of horizontal scale.

In the model given $\dfrac{\sqrt{960}}{31800} = \dfrac{1}{1026}$ (nearly), which means that one day's tides in the model would, if correctly simulated, be equivalent to a nearly three years' tidal cycle in nature.

Reynolds had laid his model bed with a uniform level of sand and was astonished and delighted to find that the tidal flow and ebb in his model were shaping accurately those features by which nature had taken long centuries to establish by her more deliberate moulding processes. Again modern model specialists are cautious about their inferences from experiment.

The problem arising in a tidal estuary must, of course, introduce factors of much greater complexity than those involved in one-way flow. Such an estuary, where range is large, presents dynamical problems, wherein slope, hydraulic radius, wetted perimeter and volume of discharge are almost constantly varying in relation to natural and tidal periods of oscillation imposed upon river flow.

It is very clear that no final resolution of the model problem in tidal rivers and estuaries is yet in sight and controversy still dominates the scene and is no doubt an agent of progress. Researches, however, have revealed certain basic relationships which have thrown much light on the scales to be adopted in models. It has been asserted that the exaggeration of the vertical scale must approximate or exceed the cube root of the denominator of the horizontal scale.

For example, if the horizontal scale chosen is 1/27000, the exaggeration for the vertical scale would be $\sqrt[3]{27000} = 30$. This can be summarized in the formulae:

$$E = X^{\frac{1}{3}} \quad \dotfill \text{(i)}$$

$$y = \frac{X}{X^{\frac{1}{3}}} = \frac{X}{E} \quad \dotfill \text{(ii)}$$

where: Horizontal scale $= \dfrac{1}{X}$ Vertical scale $= \dfrac{1}{y}$

Exaggeration of vertical scale $= E$

Reynold's model, having a horizontal scale of 1/31800 should, according to this formula, have an E of 31.6, whereas in fact he used a value of 33.2.

Unless such exaggerations are used in models, the analogous bed adjustment is inadequate as is shown by the ratio of velocities given by the formula:

$$\frac{c}{C} = \frac{1}{\sqrt{y}}$$

Where C = Velocity in nature.

c = Velocity in model.

$\dfrac{1}{y}$ = Vertical scale.

In other words, the equivalent velocity in the model is given by dividing by the square root of the denominator of the vertical scale. This can be shown from our general formula for the speed of free progressive waves where $C = \sqrt{gh}$.

Disregarding small increments of wave-height above mean level in shallow depths

$$\frac{S}{s} = \frac{\sqrt{gH}}{\sqrt{gh}} = \sqrt{\frac{H}{h}} = \sqrt{y}$$

Where S = speed of progressive wave in nature.

s = speed of similar free wave in model.

H = depth in nature.

h = depth in model.

$\dfrac{1}{y}$ = vertical scale of model.

Here no attempt is made to consider in any detail the most complex variables that arise in model work. Hydraulic mode techniques involve the same basic principles, and constants as those derived by Froude and which are used so successfully in ship models.

One may mention variable salinity, temperature and silt charge in estuaries as just three of the many difficult features bearing closely upon the carriage of silt in suspension, and the adjustment of bed features.

The researches of Dr. Gibson have shown that in the transportation of silt and other detritus the carrying power of a tidal stream varies as the sixth power of the speed and that the erosive power varies as the square or:

$$\text{Carrying power} \propto V^6$$
$$\text{Erosive power} \propto V^2$$

The relation of silt transportation to small variations in speed is clear from the above as it is obvious, for example, that the transporting power of a 2 and 2.1 knot stream would vary as

$$\frac{(2.0)^6}{(2.1)^6} = \frac{64}{86}$$

Thus when, for hydraulic reasons (say an open pile jetty or an increase of cross-section) a tidal stream is reduced from 2.1 to 2.0 knots, the *transporting* power will become reduced by about $\frac{1}{3}$, and certain material in suspension at a critical velocity will deposit.

Deposition on the convex sides of river or channel bends, and also on bars either at estuarine river-mouths or where narrow tidal harbours open out on the sea, will be understood if this fact is borne in mind. The salinity layers in such areas varying with flood and ebb stream is a problem which still awaits full solution.

Tidal models have given rise to a number of ingenious small-scale tide- and wave-making devices. The power-operated displacement plunger is the usual device, and this is suitably actuated by timed mechanisms simulating the tidal rhythm in accordance with the time-scale of the model. Other devices using the pneumatic principle have also been successfully employed.

Tidal model-makers and tidal scientists have not yet arrived at mutually satisfactory theoretical concepts, the former using very successful empirical and tentative experimental processes, whilst the latter seek to explain and tidy up discrepancies by the methods of exact quantitative analysis.

Yet despite the imponderables and gaps in our knowledge, valuable engineering projects have been aided by tidal models. Tidal phenomena, in the River Severn, for example (including

Acknowledgements to Canadian Information Service

Plate VI   Ladder Fishing in Bay of Fundy

Plate VIa   Fishing arrangement—Bay of Fundy

Acknowledgements to Mr. J. P. M. P. Pannell, M.I.C.E

Plate VII   The Old Tidal Mill—Ashlett, Southampton Water

Plate VIII   Tidal Model Building Southampton University

the bore), and elsewhere, have been successfully reproduced giving some approximation to nature which is remarkable enough, although it is not yet exact enough for tidal or model experts to acclaim as a sound theoretical analogy.

Appendix (IV) gives some details of the Southampton Tidal model initiated by the author and built at Southampton University.

The problem of two-way flow in tidal models with all the complex variations in level, range, and velocity, material in suspension, not to say salinity, still awaits satisfactory solution, but it is well to note the remarkable fact that when, in some cases, suitable adjustments between vertical and horizontal scales are arrived at, along the lines indicated, the bed material used by nature can be used in the model to give roughly analogous results.

This appears to point to some ultimate harmony underlying all the phenomena which will, no doubt, be revealed when all, or most of the data are available to the mathematical physicist who will then narrow the gap still existing, between theory and practice. The tendency now is to construct models on as large scales as are practicable and economic.

TIDAL RECORDING DEVICES

During the latter half of the nineteenth century when the increase of the draught of ships became so rapid and tidal requirements for the safe access, berthing and close scheduling of steamships more critical, the need for official automatic tide gauges at the larger ports of the world became imperative for many reasons. They were a protective measure against inaccurate assertions made by shipping companies involving claims against harbour authorities for damage or loss due to grounding in approach channels. Not less important, however, was the fact that accurate observations were a necessary foundation for the precise predictions we now use. Another valuable feature in narrow estuarine approach channels is the small temporary drop in the recorded curve caused by the passage of large vessels or high-powered tugs at excessive speeds which give a harbour authority a check on statements of time and speed. Finally, the accurate and proved astronomical predictions of our times, based upon earlier records, afford a good basis for research into the causes of the meteorological tide and the means of its prediction from contemporary synoptic weather charts.

In the ports of London, Liverpool and Southampton, automatic tide recording devices have long been required by statute, and their maintenance made the responsibility of the harbour authorities.

These demands led to the design of a sound mechanical recording device working off a float guarded by a pipe or shaft open to the sea and well below the level of lowest low water. A wire connected to this float passed up over a drum of convenient diameter with several turns, the essential tension for tautness and linearity being provided by a small counterpoise weight. (See Fig. X, 4). The movement of the float drum is geared

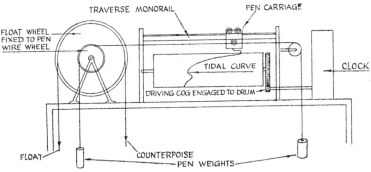

Fig. X, 4 Essential recording tide gauge

down and actuates a pen carriage moving along the recording drum driven by clockwork. The scales of float movement and time relation are adjusted to show a continuous weekly record (see Fig. X, 5).

This instrument is easily the most reliable type although there are many other principles on which gauges may be constructed. Electrical devices can and have been made, but the many difficulties involved in electrical failure or variation in voltage aggravated by exposure of contacts to weather and sea-water make the method unsatisfactory for fundamental continuous and reliable statistical observations. It is, nevertheless, useful to relay the results of mechanical gauges by electrical methods and there are signs of improving techniques.

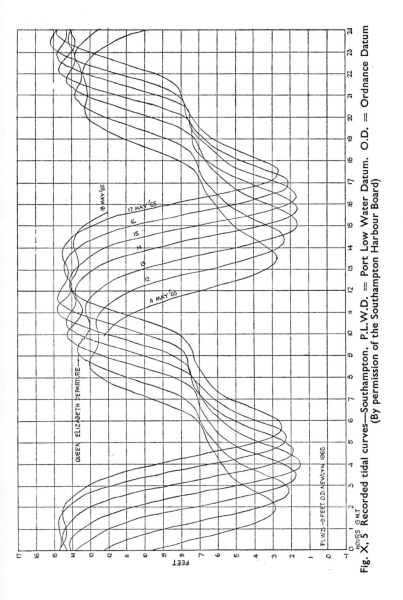

QUEEN ELIZABETH DEPARTURE →

18 MAY/65

17 MAY/65

16

15

14

13

12

11 MAY/65

P.L.W.D.—9·FEET O.D. NEWLYN 1965

FEET

HOURS GMT

Fig. X, 5 Recorded tidal curves—Southampton. P.L.W.D. = Port Low Water Datum. O.D. = Ordnance Datum
(By permission of the Southampton Harbour Board)

Another method, beloved of ingenious theorists, is the use of the pressure principle. This may be useful on hydrographic survey work where it is desired to have tidal readings at sites when it is difficult to erect a tide pole, owing to a very small beach gradient, or near steep cliffs where the sea turbulence prevents close reading or recording. A long flexible pipe is taken seaward into the water free of turbulence, fixed so as to be clear of bottom siltage, and water excluded over its whole length by pumping from the shore until pressure ceases to increase and thus balances the water head at the outlet or site of measurement. It is then possible to connect the shore end to a pressure-recording device, the varying head of water being read off continuously on a suitable scale. A U-tube containing mercury is one simple way in which this can be done. Alternatively, a resilient pressure chamber can be laid carefully at the gauge site and variations in pressure through a narrow gauge pipe read off on a suitably calibrated recorder at the shore end.

All such gauges must be checked frequently against some visual reference levels, as condensation in pipes, length of pipe, scouring, corrosion or silting up of the seaward apparatus are sources of error.

Generally speaking, pressure gauges have a very limited use for the reasons given and are not favourably regarded by seamen or hydrographic surveyors requiring continuous and accurate sea levels given by devices with only a few very obvious sources of failure.

Recording devices attached to pressure chambers or tubes are subject to many sources of error, as the actuation of calibrated pointers or pens affects results too critically for accurate recordings unless elaborate design and skilled operation are employed; this, of course, precludes their economic use as continuous statistical recorders at ports and harbours.

The visual tide gauge board, truly calibrated and levelled, is the daily check on all such mechanical, electrical or pressure recorders, although the mechanical float recorder will alone give the mean levels accurately when wave action or swell are excessive. It is, therefore, of great importance that in this reliable and proved instrument, the diameter of the inlet orifice in relation to the float pipe is neither too small for fouling nor too large to maintain reasonable stability in levels free from outside wave or swell action.

Theoretically, any wave "head" above mean level would cause a flow in feet per second equal to $\sqrt{2\,gh}$, and in practical hydraulics this value is generally reduced by about one-third. Thus, $C = 0.6\,\sqrt{2\,gh}$ (h = head in feet).

The increase in the level inside the float pipe for a given head in feet per second is, therefore:

$$\frac{\text{area of orifice}}{\text{area of float pipe}} \times 0.6\,\sqrt{2gh}$$

$$= \frac{d^2}{D^2} \times 0.6 \times 8\,\sqrt{h}\ \text{(approx.)}$$

$$= 5\,\frac{d^2}{D^2} \times \sqrt{\text{head in feet (approx.)}}$$

Where   d = diameter of orifice in feet.
        D = diameter of float pipe in feet.
More conveniently we may write:

Inches rise per second in float pipe $= \dfrac{60}{n^2}\,\sqrt{h}$ where $n = \dfrac{D}{d}$

Accordingly, when for example the diameter of the float pipe is ten times that of the orifice and the wave height is two feet above mean level, the rate of rise in inches in the float pipe or well, would be:

$$\frac{60}{100} \times 1.4 = 0.84\ \text{inches per second.}$$

For 1 foot head the value would be 0.6 inches per second, Fig. X, 6 shows the comparison of the wave action outside the pipe or well with the resultant oscillation inside. In this case the internal oscillation is less than 1 inch on either side of mean level.

In practice the period of the oscillation is generally nearer 4 seconds and with a wave-height of 1 foot above mean level the internal oscillation for such relations between orifice and well diameter is generally less than half an inch above and below mean level.

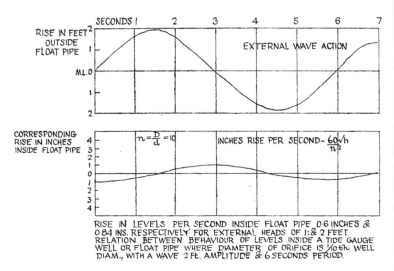

RISE IN LEVELS PER SECOND INSIDE FLOAT PIPE 0·6 INCHES &
0·84 INS. RESPECTIVELY FOR EXTERNAL HEADS OF 1:& 2 FEET.
RELATION BETWEEN BEHAVIOUR OF LEVELS INSIDE A TIDE GAUGE
WELL OR FLOAT PIPE WHERE DIAMETER OF ORIFICE IS 1/10th WELL
DIAM., WITH A WAVE 2 FL. AMPLITUDE & 6 SECONDS PERIOD.

Fig. X, 6 Effect of external surface waves upon internal levels in tide gauge wells

For 1 inch difference of level (with $\frac{D}{d} = 10$) the rate of rise in

the well would be $\frac{60}{100} \times \sqrt{0.085} = \frac{60 \times .29}{100} = 0.17$ inches

per second.

Levels, therefore, would be adjusted in a period of $\frac{1}{0.17} = 6$

seconds. As the maximum rate of rise in European waters never
exceeds 0.12 inches per second, or about 7 inches per minute,
the value of 10 for $\frac{D}{d}$ is a good one. So long as the orifice is kept

clear and the bottom of the well or pipe carried well below the
level of lowest low water, wave action will diminish at deeper
levels and decrease still further the possibility of a lag.

Finally, it is important that the float is of sufficient diameter
to ensure that the emersion due to the pull of the counterpoise
is small and a diameter of 18-24 inches brings this down to a
negligible value.

The formula, 2.15 w/d², gives the error due to emersion in inches where:

w = weight of counterpoise in ounces

and d = diameter of float in inches.

Thus for a float diameter of 18 inches and a counterpoise weight of 12 ounces required to actuate the height mechanism the error would approximately be:

$$\frac{2.15 \times 12}{324} = 0.08 \text{ inches nearly.}$$

TIDE PREDICTING MACHINES

The principle of a "summation" wire, secured at one end and rove through a system of pulleys on sheaves, each separately moved up and down vertically by the rotation of "constituent" cranks of varying radii, phase relationships, and speeds, has been described earlier and is not difficult to understand.

So long as there is no slack or stretch in the wire and no mechanical play or lag in slotted links or gears, the harmonic motion will be perfectly summed up by a pen carriage moving over a drum at the free end of the wire.

On the other hand, it is not possible to avoid all those features which must arise in such devices through friction and wear.

By a number of mechanical expedients, including the use of nickel tapes and ball-bearing pulleys, the elaborately designed and modern power-driven tide predicting machines are able to produce good results with any range of tide, maximum machine errors being less than fractions of an inch.

Plate II shows a 42 component Kelvin machine constructed in 1950 for the Liverpool Tidal Institute.

The chronological table on page 168, is taken by permission of the Hydrographer of the Navy from the Admiralty Manual of Tides, p. 131, art. 14, 13.

The installation and use of such machines requires specialist supervision and skilled mechanical operation to ensure accurate predictions. Machines have been designed to:

(a) Draw the tidal curve.

(b) Mark the axis of the curve, giving times and heights of high and low water.

(c)   Exhibit on dials the height at any time, or the times of high and low water.

In addition to these remarkable devices by which all the tides at the major ports and naval bases of the world have been predicted, the Netherlands Hydraulic Laboratory at Delft developed in 1952 a predicting device using alternating electric currents of differing frequencies and amplitudes, instead of mechanical methods, to give the harmonic synthesis for feeding into tidal models.

List of Mechanical Tide-Predicting Machines (to 1952)

Date of completion	Designation	No. of components available
1873	British Association	10
1879	Indian Association	20-24
1881	French	15-16
1882	Ferrel (U.S.A.)	19
1908	Roberts (U.S.A.)	33-40
1910	U.S.A.	37
1910	Brazilian	12
1924	Japanese	15
1916	German	20
1918	Argentine	16
1924	Japanese	15
1924	Japanese	16
1924	Portuguese	16
1924	Tidal Institute	26
1927	Brazilian	16

In more recent years a number of machines have been constructed as follows:

1939	German	62
1945	Russian	30
1947	Norwegian	30
1950	Philippine	30
1950	Tidal Institute	42
1951	Siamese	30

The last five have been designed by Dr. Doodson and the last three were made according to greatly improved designs.

In 1964 The Liverpool Tidal Institute achieved the complete substitution of mechanical predicting devices by electronic computers and I quote from their Report in 1964:

"Methods of Prediction and Analysis

The Institute has now completed the first phase in its exploitation of the digital computer for tidal work by having converted its orthodox methods of tidal analysis and prediction, suitably modified, to computer operation. The result takes the form of a family of highly efficient programs designed both for routine tasks and for research purposes.

For the prediction of high and low waters the KDF 9 prediction system has been exhaustively tested and now replaces the mechanical analogue predictors. The computations proceed by feeding into the machine a 'year tape,' containing the astronomical variables for the chosen year, and the 'port tape,' containing the harmonic constants for the chosen port. Since the computations, including re-arrangement of the output so as to conform with internationally accepted tide-table format, take no more than 2 minutes of machine time for the more complex tidal regimes, and in some cases as little as 1 minute, predictions for 100 ports for a given year can theoretically be produced in one machine run of about 3 hours. Output is on paper tape which is then fed into a specially designed Ultra tape reader-writer which produces typed copies, suitable for photolithographic reproduction, at the rate of one port per 45 minutes. Designed by Mr. Murray, the program gives a nominal accuracy of 1 minute and 0.1 foot.

Amongst the many advantages of this system are:

(a) a wide scope and complete choice of orthodox harmonic constituents for synthesis; up to 100 constituents can be used without program modification;

(b) rapidity of computation;

(c) the option of computing and adding harmonic shallow water corrections, after Doodson, to the predictions;

(d) the re-computation of the nodal corrections at monthly intervals;

(e) an appreciable reduction in human error."

The system is complicated and employs ingenious electronic

combinations in the electrical analogy to modify the normal performance of an uninterrupted current.

It appears that electronic calculating devices can now provide a satisfactory technique for the prediction of tides from the harmonic constituents without recourse to mechanical devices and their inherent difficulties, and the technical and economic limitations which once seemed to discount such a possibility have now been overcome (see pages 167, 182).

BORES

It has been shown in Chapter VII that when the velocity of a current is less than the critical value of $\sqrt{gh}$, any decreases, in width and river section along the direction of flow cause a lowering of water level.

This situation, occurring on the flood tide, clearly tends to produce a steep downward gradient or slope on the upstream side of the incoming wave.

If, however, the tide is later moving up a steeper declivity in the river bed, the flood velocity will increase up to and above $\sqrt{gh}$ when the effect of rise in bed level will now be reversed and so accentuate the rise in water level as to produce a turbulent slope, or steep wall of water travelling upstream.

Using Bernoulli's theorem, the rate of propagation of a bore can be deduced from the formula:

$$C = \left(1 + \frac{y}{D + D_1}\right) \times \sqrt{5.5\,(D + D_1)}$$

Where C = speed of bore in knots.
   y = height of bore in feet.
   D = depth before bore passes (feet).
   D_1 = depth as bore passes (feet).

It is clear from this formula that shallow depths taken together with large tidal ranges are favourable to bore formation and sudden increases in bed gradient in narrowing sections are always found at points where bores are pronounced.

Where side embankments are built to train the river at such points and the geological features permit the consequent deepening, bore features will diminish and can disappear.

The bores in the rivers Severn, Trent, and at Moncton, New Brunswick, are well known and are illustrated respectively in Plates III, IV and V.

Probably the most remarkable one in the world is that of the Chiang Tang Kiang in China which was the subject of a very accurate report by Admiral W. Usborne in the last century. At Haining the depth at springs before the passage of the bore is 5 feet, but the bore rushes past at over 16 knots as a wall of water about 11 feet high.

Using the formula for speed in knots.

$$C = \left(1 + \frac{y}{D + D_1}\right) \sqrt{5.5 \, (D + D_1)}$$

we get $\left(1 + \dfrac{11}{21}\right) \times \sqrt{5.5 \times 21}$

$$= \frac{32}{21} \times 10.75 = 16.4 \text{ knots.}$$

This is almost exactly the speed observed at Haining.

The sailors navigating the Chinese junks have developed a technique for avoiding the bore, and have built alcoves with platforms along the bank of the river into which the junks are hauled, secured by ropes, and safely ride out the worst features. The naval party under Admiral Usborne did not realize the great dangers involved when they planned their expedition, and very nearly lost their boats and lives, the situation being saved only by superb seamanship.

The anchors of the launches, after dragging when the bore took charge, were polished in such a manner as to look like silver. Bores of this sort are undoubtedly amongst the most remarkable and awe-inspiring sights in which nature abounds.

BIBLIOGRAPHY

CLARK JAMES—Grunion in Southern California, Reprint from California Fish and Game, Vol. 24, No. 1, January 1938.
Correspondence—Nature (Vol. 130, 1932, p. 23).
CHATLEY, DR. HERBERT, M.I.C.E., F.R.A.S.—The Hangchow Bore.
ALLEN, DR.—Tidal Models (Longmans, Green and Co. Ltd.).
INGLIS, SIR CLAUDE, C.I.E., M.I.C.E., etc. Tidal Models.
Tidal Models—Various papers before the Institute of Civil Engineers.
SHANKLAND, CAPTAIN E. C., R.D., R.N.R.—Modern Harbours.

CHAPTER ELEVEN

Utilization of Tidal Energy

IT HAS been calculated that the kinetic energy exerted in the rotation of the earth is of the order 3.7×10^{28} foot pounds. As the tidal phenomena of our planet is a measure of some of the work done, many attempts have been made to calculate the diminution of the earth's speed of rotation due to tidal friction over long eras. It has been deduced from such calculations that tidal friction and work done would only lengthen the solar day by a period of two or three seconds in one million years, so for the general purposes of discussion and, indeed, for estimating the effects upon posterity we may disregard this aspect of tidal energy. On the other hand, the great energy manifest in the vertical and horizontal hydraulic movement of tidal water has always stirred the imagination of the engineer and seaman.

Sailors from the earliest times have utilized buoyant craft or "camels" in salvage operations, where the tidal range is of appreciable value. This method is still used in modern times as shown in Fig. XI, 1. The sunken craft is first swept clear of

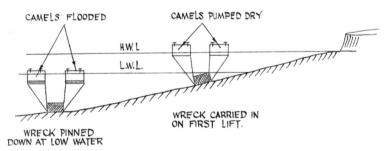

Fig. XI, I   Tidal salvage lift

top obstructions and lifting wires passed under her; buoyed camels of adequate buoyancy are then warped over her and the lifting wires passed over them and secured to stout bollards. The camels are then flooded to decrease buoyancy and augment the lift and as the tide falls to low water, lifting wires are hove taut and secured. This operation is styled "pinning down."

As the tide rises on the flood, the wreck is lifted clear of the bottom, the camels are pumped dry and at succeeding high water the wreck is towed up the salvage beach into shoal water where she grounds. At next low water the operations of pinning down and lift are repeated and the wreck eventually towed into depths shoal enough to give good surface access at low water times when the casualty can be made self-buoyant by cofferdams or bulkheads.

The tidal rise and fall of large barges, pontoon, or ships, has often appeared to the uninitiated to offer almost unlimited sources of energy which, by gearing and other devices, could be converted into mechanical power but the difficulty is the relatively slow movement in level as the following calculation will show.

Take a ship of 10,000 tons displacement and a tidal rise of 20 feet in 6 hours.

$$\text{H.P.} = \frac{W \times R \times 2240}{T \times 60 \times 33000} = \frac{WR}{884\,T}$$

Where W = Tons in weight.

R = Rise in level.

T = Period in hours.

Therefore: $HP = \dfrac{10000 \times 20}{884 \times 6} = 37.7$

This ridiculously small figure demonstrates the futility of the flotation method as a power source.

The next method to consider is the waterwheel which is more efficient than the flotation system and has been used in tide mills from early times. Mention is made of one at Dover in the Domesday Book.

London's water supply was successfully pumped up into a waterwheel borne by rafts and secured by moorings, between two of the piers of old London Bridge until demolition in 1824.

During the eighteenth century a tidal basin waterwheel was used on a site in the River Tamar in Devonshire and later replaced by turbines. Many disused tide mills are seen on rivers on the south coast of England and the one at Woodbridge is at present (1952) in use. Those at Bembridge (I.O.W.) and Ashlett Creek, Southampton Water, were once in constant use, and it is understood that the variable tidal times of working, taken with modern trade union demands have had no small part in the discontinuance of this once cheap source of tidal power for small installations (Plate VII).

The principle used was simply that of a large embanked area behind the mill outlet into which the flood tide flowed through open sluice gates, which were closed at high water. The outflow sluices were then opened and the mill operated for 4-5 hours, depending of course, on the variable range of the tide.

The work done, disallowing friction, etc., can be calculated from the following formula:

$$\text{H.P.} = \frac{37,000,000 \times 64\,\text{AR} \times \frac{1}{2}\text{R}}{60 \times 33,000 \times \text{T}} \qquad \text{(i)}$$

$$= \frac{600\,\text{AR}^2}{\text{T}} \text{ (nearly)} \qquad \text{(ii)}$$

Where A = Area of enclosed basin in nautical or geographical
             square miles.
       R = Tidal range.
       T = Period of outflow in hours.

(In (i) it will be observed that 37,000,000 square feet is taken as 1 square nautical mile).

If we take, for example, a 10-foot fall in 5 hours for one-quarter of a square mile tidal enclosure of uniform depth and allow 80 per cent efficiency we have:

$$\text{H.P.} = 80 \left(\frac{600 \times 0.25 \times 100}{5} \right) = 2400$$

The above formulae show that the power developed is proportional to the area of the basin and the square of the range (or, more correctly, of the available effective head).

The eclipse of the tidal mill did not obscure the basic principle which has been modernized in the basin-cum-turbine proposals elaborated since the middle of the eighteenth century by British and French engineers, anxious to use the large tidal ranges around their respective coasts. The single-basin system, employing a single reservoir, works on the same principle as the tide mill except that efficient modern turbines would be employed, instead of the archaic waterwheel, its crude prototype.

The single-basin method is generally designed for the ebb tidal period of semi-diurnal tides, the turbines commencing work on the ebb about 1 hour before low water using the head provided by enclosing the previous high water level.

As the water runs off, the level in the basin, and consequently the head, diminishes; this was a great difficulty until the design of turbines permitted high efficiency to be maintained over a wide head variation. This is due to the variable pitch propeller turbine which can operate efficiently under heads varying between 7 and 47 feet, a remarkable achievement.

The proposed Severn Barrage is an example of the single-basin scheme and turbines of about 30,000 h.p. output have been designed to run over an average head of 25 feet (half the spring range) at a speed of 50 r.p.m. The Kaplan variable pitch type of water turbine is employed in the design, the angle of the turbine blades being altered as requisite in adjustment to the varying head.

Unless the range is very great, as in the case of the upper reaches of the Severn, the altering high water times and the variation in range between springs and neaps (3.5 to 1 in the case of the proposed Severn scheme), give an intermittent supply necessitating elaborate devices for the storage of energy and this is undoubtedly one of the reasons for hesitancy in advancing beyond the design stage.

The double-basin system is an attempt to ensure a more continuous power output by employing two adjacent basins. One basin is filled from the tideway through sluices on the flood. The other basin having been emptied on the previous ebb can now be filled from the charged basin through turbines and power generated from the flow.

The high-level basin inlets can be so adjusted as to keep the level above $\dfrac{2R}{3}$, whilst the low-level basin is so adjusted that the level is never allowed to rise above $\frac{1}{3}$ R—where R = range.

The double-basin system, therefore, ensures a continuous power output and eliminates the need for energy storage but requires increased tidal-basin area and is, like all the other systems, adversely affected by the bi-monthly small neap tidal range, in semi-diurnal areas.

It should, however, be added that the efficiency of single-basin systems can be nearly doubled by the alternate use of duplicate turbines arranged to work under a constant head, one system operating on the flood tide and the other on the ebb.

We may tabulate the various systems in recapitulation:

System	Features	Relative Tidal Basin area for given H.P.
Single Basin	Ebb L.W. discharge	A
	Ebb constant head discharge	3A
	Alternate constant head flood/ebb discharge	1.5A
Double Basin	Constant mean head $=2/3R$	4A

A double-basin project has been proposed for the Bay of Fundy out of whose 3 miles wide entrance more than 100 million h.p. hours run to waste during the ebb and flow of each tide. It is estimated that 200 million dollars would be required for this project, at least one-quarter of the amount being needed for dredging alone.

Speaking generally, it would seem that the enthusiasm aroused in engineers by the great hydraulic forces in tidal estuaries of large range has nearly always diminished when close investigation of tidal behaviour revealed the many variables requiring to be covered by successful design. The economic obstacles involved and the discontinuity of output have further conspired to keep major tidal projects from venturing much farther than the drawing-board and tidal model stage.

The exploitation of large ranges for tidal energy projects has been considered for many sites including Frobisher Bay on

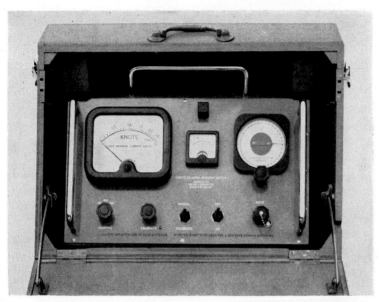

Acknowledgements to Kelvin Hughes Ltd.

Plate IX   Direct Reading Current Meter (Inboard recording Console)

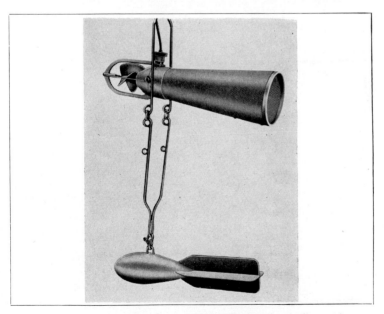

Plate X   Direct Reading Current Meter (Outboard propeller unit)

Plate XI Photograph of Rance Barrage

Acknowledgements to Electricité de France

the coast of Baffin Island; the mouth of the Amazon; the Gulf of San Jose, Argentina; a region in the strait of Magellan and in France the fiord of Aber Vrac'h: the Bay of the Somme and above all the Bay of Mont-Saint Michel and the Chausey Islands.

All these, including the Severn project, in Great Britain, have been abandoned for a variety of reasons but at last a scheme has actually been commenced (in 1960) by Electricity France at the mouth of the River Rance near St. Malo where the average and maximum spring range values are $37\frac{1}{2}$ and $43\frac{1}{2}$ feet respectively.

The problem, hitherto confined to providing adequate basin area for uni-directional flow, now appears to have been transformed by the conception of reversible sets combining turbine and alternator and called "bulbs."

These comprise 24 hermetically sealed units sited on the bottom of the tidal access channel and are capable of operating both on flood and ebb. The propellers of variable pitch can be "feathered", as in the Kaplan design, to maintain uniform rates under varying "heads," or alternatively to allow free passage of water.

The site is shown in Plate XI and the varying cycles that can be utilized are indicated in Fig. XI, 2.

The following five types of operation provided for exploiting all tidal conditions are illustrated as follows:

(i) Water enters basin on flood providing electrical supply.
(ii) At end of flood energy is "borrowed back" from electrical network, turning turbines for "overfill" level.
(iii) Water leaves basin on ebb providing electrical energy.
(iv) At end of ebb energy is borrowed from network to give "over-emptying" level.
(v) Turbine blades adjusted to allow "free flow" as requisite.

It is estimated that the annual output will be about 540 million K.W.H.—about half the output of one of the French Rhine power stations—yet the St. Malo set will be the first and only tidal power station likely to come into economic operation it is anticipated by 1967.

Scientific men have never regarded tidal energy projects as either impossible, or even unlikely and some have envisaged them as ultimate necessities when scarcity and the increasing costs of coal and oil become embarrassing to mankind.

M

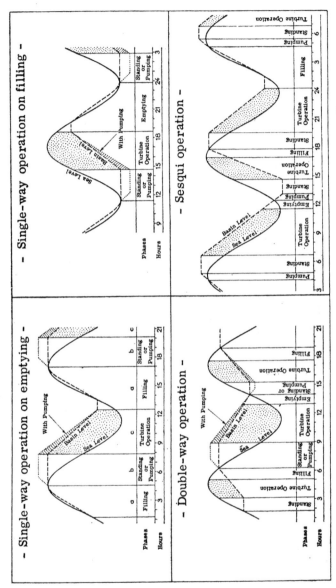

Fig. XI, 2   Diagram showing sequence of operations at Rance hydro-electric installation

But the harnessing of universal energy by processes of nuclear fission now make it almost inevitable that this new and dramatic source of energy may be rendered available to an increasing degree during the next twenty years, and so anticipate the decay of those solar forces latent in the oil and coal sources of our planet.

Thus it may prove that the mathematical physicist has struck the final blow against those brave dreams of stupendous tidal projects so long beloved of seamen and engineers, but now rendered unnecessary by the fact that man himself has become a cosmic force.

It may well be that the geophysical possibilities inherent in the use of atomic energy may enable the tidal engineer and scientist to blast with a yet unattainable precision, great earth ducts joining coastal areas, where there is no tide, to those adjacent, where tidal ranges are considerable and thus extend the advantages of tidal conservancy to inland sites.

One thing is certain.

The value of tidal energy is at a maximum when applied to the transport problems of large ships and the transference of useful tidal ranges well inside coastal fringes by scientifically controlled excavation, may yet be accomplished by unprecedented feats of cosmic engineering allied to tidal research.

CHAPTER TWELVE

The future of tidal research

IT NOW remains to consider the directions along which tidal research workers may move in their endeavour to bring all the phenomena within the frame of ultimate mathematical exposition without reference to observation. Clearly we have a long way to go before this state of knowledge is achieved. The researches of the last fifty years have made tremendous strides in the observation, analysis, and prediction of world tides, in laying bare the three ingredients of the tidal mystery, namely, stationary wave motion, resonance, and gyration, but it is still true that predictions must be based on reliable quantitative records of observed performance; for the frictional modifications of the primary wave are as yet, incalculable from fundamental postulates. Furthermore, the meteorological surge is often a major and unexpected feature of tidal perturbations and seismic surges "arrive" often without official warning.

Again, as we have noted, co-tidal charts for the great oceans are still based upon inferences with slender quantitative foundations and those of the Pacific still await even tentative construction apart from brilliant mathematical treatment which, however, cannot as yet compute frictional modifications. The tidal streams in the oceans await accurate observation *at all depths* and the surface currents shown on charts are often derived from the difference between the astronomical and dead reckoning positions of ships at sea—a method, even since the advent of gyroscopic compasses, fraught with much uncertainty and error and nearly always unrelated to tidal rhythms.

Clearly tidal research must seek instruments capable of making accurate quantitative records of the vertical tidal movement in the large oceans as well as the tidal streams at different depths and neither of these problems is as simple as might appear.

OCEANIC TIDES

Determination of the rise and fall of the tide in very deep water presents as yet insuperable problems, apart from observations on remote oceanic islands. No pressure device has yet proved satisfactory for many complex reasons.

As is well known, an echo-sounding oscillator on the sea bottom directed vertically upwards can record the level of the water surface by reflection, and it is possible that a submersible pressure chamber may be designed to sink to the bottom, release upwards a "wide-beam" oscillator on a short antenna, and take large-scale inverted echo-sounding readings of surface levels against time for a period of days, after which it could automatically surface for recovery and inspection.

It would seem that only simultaneous observations and accurate records, systematically co-ordinated over wide areas, could solve the problem of providing quantitative data for charting the co-tidal systems of the oceans. Mathematical prognosis indicates that the Pacific Ocean abounds in amphidromic systems, but the effect of friction must greatly modify theoretical values.

USE OF TIDAL MODELS

In areas adjacent to the English Channel such as the Solent, it would seem that tidal models may throw light upon the ancillary hydraulic factors modifying the external tidal waves. The construction of these models would necessarily be preceded by the collection of accurately observed data and a more complete understanding of the scale factors involved than is available in the present state of our knowledge.

METEOROLOGICAL SURGES

Undoubtedly the prediction of the meteorological tide is making remarkable progress in some areas and the technique successfully evolved for the Thames and North Sea areas by Dr. Doodson and R. J. Corkan of the Liverpool Tidal Institute, indicate the possibility of absolute prediction, dependent, of course upon the accuracy of the meteorological data provided as a basis. By relating the isobaric disposition and movement to stationary wave periods in the North Sea and having full and immediate access to the readings of widely scattered and representative tide gauges in this area, results can be analysed and predicted with some accuracy.

When basic analysis is complete, suitable organization and co-ordination may provide immediacy of prediction for the many purposes required. This method will undoubtedly improve in accuracy and be extended to the English Channel and Irish Sea, and the time may come when the increment of meteorological surge, to be applied to the astronomical predictions for local high water, will be available with weather forecasts. Storm surges will then no longer surprise harbour authorities and other bodies whose interests are often seriously affected by sudden increases in sea level accompanied by wave action.

SEISMIC SURGES

To a lesser degree the ability to predict surges arising from remote seismic disturbances estimated at observatories, may well become possible by comprehensive co-ordination aiming at relative immediacy in prediction. Recent results at some sites indicate that stationary wave phenomena and resonance may enable the results of such superimposed oscillations to be computed fairly closely for frequency and amplitude.

PREDICTION AND ANALYSIS

There is no doubt that electronic methods can now be applied to the analysis and summation of the tidal constituents hitherto solved by mechanical devices, the several following difficulties existing in 1952 having now been largely overcome:

   (i) Speeds of constituents must be given to at least one part in a million to compete with existing machines.
   (ii) A very high technique is required to achieve the required precision for each constituent.
   (iii) Maintenance and replacement of cathode ray tubes and other units was a problem.
   (iv) Provision of skilled operators.
   (v) A cost of over ten times that of operating existing (1952) machines.
   (vi) Unacceptable possibilities of error arising from causes outlined above.

It would appear that the admirable 42-component machine used in the Liverpool Tidal Institute (Plate XI) represents a final stage in the technique of *mechanical* harmonic tidal prediction. Whilst, as has been stated, direct prediction from the widest range of constituents will not give results according exactly with actuality, such results augmented by the system of harmonic corrections invented by Dr. Doodson have, in the case of Southampton, given prediction to a degree of precision more than satisfying the rigorous scheduling requirements for the sailing and arrival of the world's deepest draught liners at that port. Nevertheless it is clear that electronic methods for prediction must increasingly supersede the mechanical, and at the time of writing the immense advantage of electronic computation is indicated by the extract from the 1964 Report of the Liverpool Tidal Institute quoted on page 169.

TRACTIVE FORCES

Whilst the forces that produce the tide are precisely known, the term "gravitational" is only a descriptive device to indicate the behaviour of cosmic tensions, the ultimate nature of which we are as yet unable to understand.

To say that the mutual action of bodies over a distance varies as the product of their masses and inversely as the square of their distance, only describes the mode or degree of action. It is possible that new cosmic discoveries will reveal many features bearing upon the operation of those tractive forces which raise the tides.

Yet despite the many avenues of tidal research now opened up to us, the mathematician must be given his premises and these are the fundamental quantitative measurements he so earnestly seeks from the surveyor, seaman and engineer.

The amount of work and costs involved in the necessary design of the many necessary instruments and devices, their development and trials, together with their successful employment by co-ordinated international oceanographic research, appears to be stupendous and in the present state of world affairs their supply is unlikely. Yet as a paradox, it is remarkable and even sinister to notice how the great forward surges of knowledge have come out of the tensions and crises arising out of the conflicts of men.

Whilst the collection of data in the oceans still promises to be a laborious task, it will provide the basis for completing the revolution in tidal science which has been proceeding with increasing impetus during the last century.

BIBLIOGRAPHY

GIBSON, PROFESSOR A. H.—Natural Sources of Energy, 1913.
MARMER—The Tide.
DARWIN—The Tides.

Summary of main formulae and data

Chapter Two

$Fx \dfrac{mm^1}{d^2}$ (Attractive force between particles)

Moon's attraction on particle of unit mass at centre of earth—

$$g \cdot \dfrac{M}{E} \cdot \dfrac{e^2}{x^2}$$

Tractive force $T = 1.5\,g \cdot \dfrac{M}{E} \cdot \dfrac{e^3}{r^3}\,Sin\,2\theta$

Chapter Three

Simple Standing Oscillation: $T = \dfrac{2l}{gh} - (1, 2, 3, \ldots\ldots)$

Formulae for free progressive wave:

$$\text{Speed f.p.s.} = \sqrt{gh}$$

Wave length in nautical miles $= 8.25T\,\sqrt{D}$ (approx.)

$(T = \text{period in hours})$

$(D = \text{depth in fathoms})$

Formulae for stationary waves:

Where l = length in nautical miles of gulf

$\quad\quad D$ = mean depth in fathoms

$\quad\quad T$ = period in hours

$$l = 4.1\,T\,\sqrt{D} \quad\quad\quad\quad\quad\quad \text{(i)}$$

$$T = \dfrac{l}{4.1}\,\sqrt{D} \quad\quad\quad\quad\quad\quad \text{(ii)}$$

Gyroscopic effect of earth's rotation $= 2m.w.\sin$ latitude

Chapter Five

Height at any time of any harmonic constituent

$$= H.Cos\,(nt - g)$$

Chapter Six

Formula for theoretical elevation of sea level resulting from a moving atmospheric pressure system:

$$y = \frac{13\ (29.8 - P)}{1 - K^2/68\ D}$$

Where y = Elevation in feet
       K = Speed in knots
       D = Depth in fathoms.

A new development in current meters

Device for Simultaneous Plotting

BY A. J. WOODS AND D. H. MACMILLAN

Reprinted from "The Dock and Harbour Authority" No. 469, Vol. XL, November, 1959

FOR A very long time Hydrographic Surveyors, Hydraulic Engineers and Conservancy Officers, have been looking for a reliable current meter that would enable an observer in a tautly moored surface ship to plot a relatively simultaneous profile of accurately determined directions and rates of water movement, at a series of selected depths within relatively short intervals of time.

In general it may be said that a number of devices using propellers, anemometer type "buckets", and others using the principle of angular displacement, have achieved fairly accurate estimates of the rate of flow, but none have hitherto enabled an observer to determine direction or "set" to closer than 10°, due, of course, to limitations inherent in the ordinary magnetic element.

Furthermore, the inevitable delay in interpreting the results at each selected depth has, hitherto, made it impossible for an observer to obtain accurate results, say, within a period of five minutes, for a number of depths between surface and sea bed.

In gauging river or estuarine flow for estimation of volume of transfer, it has for long been a crying need to be able to plot direction and rate of flow as nearly as possible simultaneously for a series of depths at stations selected across a given channel section. It is certain that any reliable device that makes this possible will have an assured future in hydraulic research when performance is confirmed. It is essential in such work that field data should be precise and instrumentation has not yet kept pace with ideal requirements, especially in model work.

Naval Hydrographers, knowing the limitation of mechanical

devices for tidal stream measurements have found in the behaviour of the vertical current spar of uniform section, immersed
to 30-ft. depth, the best practical method for ascertaining values
affecting ships whose draughts approximate this figure. The
tidal stream stations shown on Admiralty charts accordingly
give information based on such determinations at intervals referred to the times of high water at the nearest standard
ports.

The writers accordingly decided to carry out trials near the
postion of Calshot Light Vessel, at the entrance to Southampton
Water, using the new direct reading current meter designed and
made by Kelvin Hughes, and arranged for observations to cover
continuously, and at short intervals *two* consecutive Spring tidal
cycles of equal range monitored during daylight hours by vertical
spar observations.

The mean depth of the spar used was 12-ft. (or half the immersed depth) and the current meter was set to operate at 15-ft.
depth; it was, of course, realised the results were not necessarily comparable, as a mean performance over a 24-ft. depth
range might not accord precisely with the behaviour of a thin
layer at, or near, its mean depth.

The observing ship was moored tautly in a position 146°
(True) from Calshot Castle (Centre —)—5,600-ft.—in a depth
of 38-ft. at low water springs (Fig. 1).

Continuous readings at the depths given were commenced on
Wednesday, 22nd April, 1949, and the following criteria for
judging results were decided upon:

(a) The result covering the *two* tidal cycles (one superimposed
on the other for comparison) and plotted in time in relation
to the occurrence of local low water at Calshot (a fairly sharp
inverted peak occurring at this time) should compare favourably if the instrument is consistent in behaviour and readings
accurately taken. This, of course, pre-supposes equal tidal
ranges and similar weather conditions. Fortunately the
latter were consistently ideal.

(b) The curves of direction and rate should, when plotted, show
consistent rates of change throughout, and not require much
"smoothing," thus illustrating the tolerances to be expected
in the practical use of the instrument.

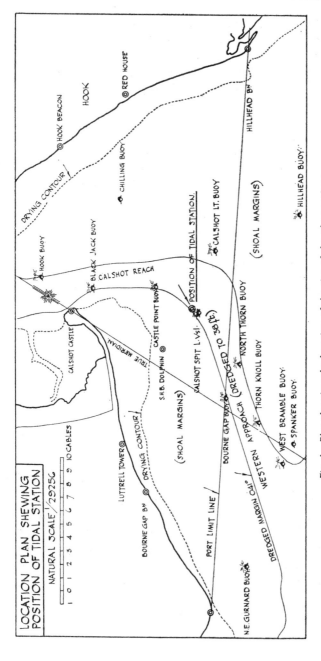

Fig. 1   Plan showing the location of the site of the observations

(c) The spar determinations should show good approximate agreement with instrumental results in rate, and also in direction, after correcting the magnetic readings for local variation (in this case 8½°W.).

(d) The recorded features should show consistently and correctly over both cycles—i.e. over 25½ hours—the hydraulic peculiarities characterising local estuarine flow at the site. It should be remembered that the Calshot area stands in a zone of transition between the tidal regime in Southampton Water, which is strictly in phase with local tidal rise and fall, and that obtaining in the Solent axis which is not, but depends absolutely on the hydraulic "balance" between the altering sea levels at the eastern and western entrances of the Solent, that is at Spithead and the Needles, respectively.

(e) It was decided not to take profiles of rates at different depths on this particular trial, but rather to anticipate this procedure at a later stage by experiments to ascertain the practical seamanship necessary for best results in handling the new instrument.

The console, which is very simple in presentation, was mounted without difficulty in the survey ship, and the meter suspended from a yard-arm rigged in crutches athwart the deckhead plotting cabin.

It was found that reading at intervals of five minutes, or even less, could be delegated to an intelligent seaman after the simple adjustments and switching were mastered, no skill whatever being needed either in manipulation, or interpretation, as the dial indications in speed and rate appeared in a very obvious and uncomplicated manner. Incidentally, the spar observations are much more complicated, and required experience and surveying skill for accurate determinations. The direct reading meter merely required a knowledge of the few switch controls, ability to make two dial readings, and a log book in which continuous readings of direction and rate could be recorded in comfort, and without any exposure to weather. Had readings over, say, five minutes, and at five-foot depth intervals been required, this would present little difficulty after the necessary rig had been perfected.

The accompanying diagram (Fig. 2) shows all the resulting data, plotted and presented for ready comparison. This is very consistent, and appears completely to confirm the performance claimed for this instrument.

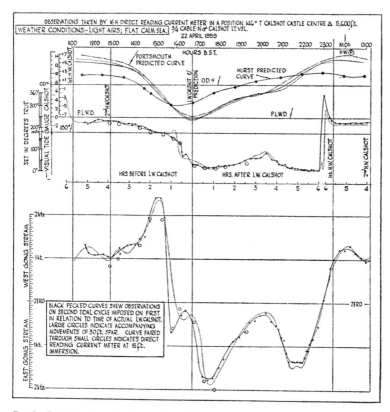

Fig. 2 Diagram showing the results of the meter; both cycles being related to the instant of Low Water at Calshot. All relevant data, bearings and checks are shown

The following two features will be especially noted in the plot of all the relevant data:

(a) The two curves provided by the instrument in relation to low water at Calshot, although taken on successive cycles are, in fact, almost identical in shape and general features, thus indicating the consistency of the two sets of observations under the same hydraulic conditions.

(b) The large circles in the diagram indicating the accompanying results of the spar drifts show very reasonable conformity with the independent results of the instruments on both tidal cycles, both in direction and rate.

It is also interesting to observe the relation of the Hurst and Portsmouth vertical curves plotted at the top of the diagram in correct time relation to the tidal stream observation.

It is interesting to note also the peak of maximum velocity occurring for a short period near $1\frac{1}{2}$ hours before low water at Calshot, as well as the rapid change in direction of the tidal stream close to the instant occurring soon afterwards when the Portsmouth tidal levels begin to fall below those at Hurst. The reason for this peak is the coincidence of the West-going tidal stream with the maximum out-flow from Southampton Water, which occurs $1\frac{3}{4}$ hours before low water at Calshot.

The alteration later of the direction of the tidal stream from East-going to West-going occurs rather more slowly after the rising levels at the Portsmouth entrance overtake those at the Hurst Narrows.

If all the features in the diagram are taken together, it will be seen that they show very consistent harmony between the behaviour of the vertical and horizontal water movements.

Incidentally, it would be very easy to miss the sharp peak above mentioned occurring for a short period near $1\frac{1}{2}$ hours before low water at Calshot, without the aid of this instrument, which enables the co-ordinates of the curve to be plotted so intimately; the spar observations, in fact, do very nearly miss it altogether.

The result of all these observations and conclusions demonstrate the unprecedented consistency and ease with which the direct reading current meter can be used, to give a full delineation of the tidal movement.

In addition, if observations at different levels below the surface are included, this can be achieved with ease and greatly improve the accuracy with which the transfer of water movements might be estimated.

Technical Description

An account of these tidal measurements and their implications would be incomplete without a description of the principle instrument employed. This current meter was one of a few pre-production models of the Kelvin Hughes new direct reading current meter whose inception came about in this way. An extensive review of existing methods of current measurement showed that the most commonly used instruments measured only the amount of water flowing by over a given period of time from which the average speed could be computed using a graph or calibration table. Many current meters needed to be hauled to the surface to be read. Some needed to be started and stopped by the sending of messenger weights down the suspension wire. Others needed the operator to count clicks in a telephone earpiece against a stop watch, and a few gave their results in the form of a tape which had to be interpreted to get the speed of flow. There was a real need for a current meter which would show the speed of flow directly on a dial.

A meter was accordingly constructed consisting of an underwater gear and an indicating unit, showing the speed on a dial of a micro-amperemeter.

This was tried out in the water of the Thames Estuary, and found to respond very rapidly to changes in the speed of the water. The movement of the pointer was very lively, especially when the meter was near the bottom, when it seemed possible to detect the turbulence of the water rolling over bottom obstructions. It was realised that this rapid response would be useful, but that, for some purposes, a slow response would be preferred, and a damping control was accordingly added to give more damping when needed.

Having achieved direct reading of speed the next step was to attempt direct reading for direction of flow also. The firm of Kelvin Hughes have, for many years, made gyro-magnetic compasses for aircraft in which the gyro is monitored by the signals from a sensitive magnetic device placed in a good magnetic situation, for example, in the wing tip. This element is called a "Fluxgate," and has been developed to a very high degree of reliability. One of these units was then mounted in the underwater part of the new current meter and the necessary circuits

N

built into the indicator unit. It was found possible to correct the magnetic deviations so that they amounted to less than one degree, and, assuming ordinary accuracy of construction of the underwater gear, it could be safely assumed that the direction of flow indicated would not in practice have an error greater than 1½ degrees. This accuracy of direction measurement is much superior to that normally attained with current meters. The reading of the new current meter, "D.R.C.M." for short, is very simple and rapid, and does not need the attention of specially skilled people. After switching on the left-hand dial quickly and directly shows the speed. The centre dial will show an imbalance to one side or the other (Plate IX). The knob beneath the right-hand dial, having been pressed and turned until the centre dial pointer shows somewhere near the centre zero, the pointer on the right-hand dial gives the "magnetic" direction of flow, that is, the angle between the direction of flow and the local magnetic meridian, to the degree of accuracy mentioned above.

The underwater gear (Plate X) consists of a central fish-shaped body which bears four guards which serve to support the forward propeller bearing, and to protect the propeller from damage. The tail of the meter is conical in form, and is made of perforated aluminium coated with a plastic paint. It has been found that this conical tail causes the axis of the meter to stream in the current very accurately, whereas it is common for other current meters to yaw badly at the higher speeds. In spite of this good streaming the drag is very little greater than is experienced, for example, with the Roberts current meter with its tail consisting of four fins intersecting in a cross. The propeller runs in low friction bearings made of "P.T.F.E."—Polytetrafluorethylene—which is an excellent material for bearing where, as in the present application, there is abundant cooling water. The body of the meter is completely sealed, and is filled to capacity with oil. A metal bellows takes care of changes in the volume of the oil due to temperature and pressure variations. The body contains the magnetic detector element and the necessary corrector magnets, as well as the cam and contacts for the speed measuring circuit. There is no mechanical connection between the inside of the body and the propeller. The necessary drive is by means of a magnetic coupling one half of which is in the propeller hub, and the other inside the body, mounted on the same shaft as the contact cam. The electrical connection is through a watertight gland at the top of the meter body. The meter is mounted on trunnions supported in a brass, hanger, to which a short length of brass chain, with the required length of supporting cord, is shackled. The meter is balanced to remain horizontal in waters of different densities, by an adjustable balance weight provided in the tail.

The indicator unit is connected to the underwater gear by a length of 6-core screened cable. All the electric power required comes from ordinary dry batteries mounted in the back of the unit, the whole gear being entirely self-contained and independent of outside power supplies. It can therefore be used anywhere. The first prototype was used at Halley Bay in the Antarctic. Immediately afterwards it was sent to the Persian Gulf where it performed very well, and, because of its rapid and direct method of use, saved a lot of observer's time. The rotation of the propeller, driving a contact arm, causes intermittent electric pulses to operate a relay in the indicator unit. This controls a circuit which ensures that the voltage across a capacitance depends on the speed of recurrence of these pulses. The meter measuring this voltage is then scaled in knots in accordance with the results obtained from tests in a ship tank at various constant speeds.

The direction sensing device—the "Fluxgate"—consists of two elements mounted parallel to the axis of the current meter and two elements across the axis. All four elements are mounted on a frame suspended from gymbals, and are consequently always horizontal. The signals from these two pairs of elements depend upon the angle which they make with the earth's magnetic meridian, and are eventually fed to a resolver. When the resolver rotor is turned until a balance is achieved, as shown on the centre meter, the direction pointer, which is fixed to the rotor, will then indicate on the circle the direction towards which the water is flowing. Supposing the water is flowing to 045° magnetic a balance could also in theory be obtained at 225° magnetic. In practice, however, this ambiguity of reading is prevented because the indicator unit contains an amplifier which feeds a signal to one or other of two solenoids depending on the phase of the signals from the magnetic detector. These solenoids operate ratchets on a gear wheel connected to the direction pointer, which are so set as to prevent the setting knob being turned in any but the correct direction to find the true null position, and thus the proper direction reading. When the pointer is only a few degrees on either side of the correct reading the amplified signals are too weak to operate the ratchets, and the operator can make his final setting in the usual way by moving the knob a little in either direction until the small meter indicates balance. Although this sounds very involved it is not so. Readings of speed, direction, and time, can be made and written down at intervals of as little as one minute, if desired.

Because of the simplicity and rapid reading of the D.R.C.M. it can be used for taking a profile of the water speeds and directions at different depths. When the flow shows little change readings can be infrequent. When conditions begin to change quickly readings can be taken very frequently. Because the speed device is entirely independent of the direction unit, the direction of flow can still be obtained accurately, even when the current is too slow to turn the propeller. This occurs at a little over 0.10 knots.

Referring to the illustration of the plot of the results obtained at Calshot, some points surrounded by little circles will be seen. These indicate results which were obtained with a vertically floating wooden spar, 30-ft. long, of which 24-ft. was immersed. The speed of drift of this spar was obtained by measuring the length of calibrated distance line run out in one minute. The directions were obtained by sextant angles between the spar and known landmarks. Although it does not necessarily follow that the drift of such a spar will correspond exactly with the indications of a current meter at 15-ft. depth of immersion, yet the agreement in direction and rate shown in these experiments is really striking and confirmatory. The current meter can, of course, give readings much more frequently than those obtained from the spar, and, if desired, it can be hauled up, or down, to give readings at several depths nearly simultaneously.

Determination of mean sea level

THE USUAL method has been to record levels at solar or lunar hourly intervals and divide the sum by the total interval.

The errors involved in terms of H. of M_2 and S_2 are as follows:

Solar Day Cycle	Lunar Day Cycle
24 hours M_2 error $= 0.035$	25 hours S_2 error $= 0.04$

Neither method is ideal.

A valuable formular which reduces errors in main harmonic constituents to the third decimal place is given in Admiralty Manual of Tides, p. 111, using 38 hourly intervals, a system of multipliers and a diviser into the summation of products for M.S.L. of 30.

Here is the Table:

Multipliers for Mean Sea Level
Divisor = 30

t	Multiplier	t	Multiplier	t	Multiplier
0	1	13	1	26	1
1	0	14	0	27	0
2	1	15	2	28	2
3	0	16	1	29	0
4	0	17	1	30	1
5	1	18	2	31	1
6	0	19	0	32	0
7	1	20	2	33	1
8	1	21	1	34	0
9	0	22	1	35	0
10	2	23	2	36	1
11	0	24	0	37	0
12	1	25	1	38	1

To compute M.S.L.;

(i) Set down the 39 hourly heights.

(ii) Apply multipliers to each height.

(iii) Add all products.

(iv) Summation of products $\div$ 30 = M.S.L. value.

The Southampton tidal model

BY D. H. MACMILLAN

Published in R.I.C.S. Journal, November, 1958

AS A great deal of publicity has been given to the subject of tidal models during the last half-century, it may be of interest to consider the use of a model by a hydrographic surveyor charged with the duty of solving certain problems of tidal behaviour peculiar to Southampton Water and the Solent area.

1. General Tidal Appreciation

It will be appreciated that modern methods of harmonic tidal prediction at Southampton involve over 24 normal constituents, and even then special corrections are necessary to achieve adequate precision for modern requirements. As the numerical constituents into which the graphical curve of height against time has been analysed do not themselves represent the physical features producing the curve, it will be apparent that the complex causes of the remarkable—and supremely favourable—tidal regime of the Southampton and Solent areas are not yet fully known.

A co-tidal chart of the English Channel illustrating the lunar M_2 tide at new or full moon ($1\frac{1}{2}$ days before maxima) see Fig. III, 12) gives ranges of 6 and 10 feet at the western (Hurst) and eastern entrances of the Solent area, respectively, with a remarkable rotation of the co-tidal lines on a rough "centre" north-west and inshore of the Isle of Wight, high waters occurring at the Eastern entrance roughly one hour later than at the western entrance. A long high water stand occurs at both entrances, that of the Hurst entrance being one hour longer than at the other, and lasting nearly three hours at the end of which time both levels fall together.

Simultaneous curves at Hurst, Calshot and Nab (off the eastern entrance of the Isle of Wight) related to Ordnance Datum (Newlyn), are illustrated in Fig. III, 26, where the following features may be noted:

(i) From about two hours before high water at Portsmouth to roughly four hours after, the levels at the eastern entrance of the Solent duct are higher than those at the western, *irrespective of whether the actual levels are rising or falling.* As the difference amounts to nearly four feet at the time of high water (Portsmouth), rudimentary principles indicate a *westerly* flow throughout this period attaining maximum rate at that time—some 20 minutes after the time of culmination at Calshot, or just high water at Southampton. This agrees with observations at tidal stations situated throughout the whole duct, and shown on Admiralty Charts 394 and 2040.

(ii) On the other hand as low waters occur within half an hour of each other at *each* entrance, and the Hurst (western) levels at those times are about 2 feet higher than the eastern, flow in the Solent duct must be *easterly* and at maximum rate at the nearly simultaneous time of low water slack outside each entrance. The many observations of tidal streams in the Solent duct shown on Admiralty Charts 394 and 2040 confirm this reasoning.

(iii) It is therefore obvious that the direction and rate of the tidal streams in the axis of the Solent are not in phase with the behaviour of tidal levels, and that the tidal streams are determined by the alternating hydraulic "head" at eastern and western entrances *irrespective of the upward and downward movement of levels.*

(iv) While the behaviour of the tidal streams *well inside* Calshot, in Southampton Water, will be in phase with vertical movement (i.e., rise with inflow, fall with outflow) the situation off Calshot itself will be a complex of both features, and the streams at this point of transition will not be rectilinear but almost rotatory. Observation confirms this, as the Solent features cause a semi-rotatory swing off Calshot light-vessel over an arc from 170 degrees through west to 030 degrees (True). (See Fig. VII, 3).

Harmonic analysis recognises the fact that the normal relation of the phases of the M_2 and M_4 constituents for double high waters, in the case of the Southampton curve, are altered by about 180 degrees, thus causing the unusual, and incidentally very valuable, long period of "flood and stand" as well as the very short ebb with its dominant scouring outflow. The Admiralty Manual of Tides attributes this remarkable reversal of the normal duration of flood and ebb in estuaries as possibly due to the two entrances to the Solent, and a study of the physical facts noted above would seem definitely to confirm this. (Admiralty Manual of Tides, pages 224-5).

2. The Problem Requiring Solution

Having outlined the fundamental principles governing tidal streams inside the Isle of Wight, I will now proceed to the problem requiring solution by model.

During 1956 the Southampton Harbour Board was approached by an interest considering the establishment of an oil installation on the eastern side of the entrance to Southampton Water off Calshot (Fig. 1).

After preliminary discussions with the local seamen, pilots, and others vitally concerned, a possible position for a dredged area was provisionally agreed upon, subject, of course, to many further studies, and a full-scale Government inquiry which has not yet been held or even requested at this stage. (See Figs. 1 and 7).

The area shown involved a proposal for the extensive deepening by over 20 feet of an exposed foreshore adjacent to a very stable, and deep, dredged channel requiring little or no maintenance. This raised several questions affecting local conservancy, including the following:

  (i) Would deepening to 37 feet below mean low water springs unseal a shingle reservoir of a grade capable of being moved into the adjacent navigable channels by post-dredging tidal streams?

 (ii) How would the tidal stream directions and rates in fact be affected by dredging this extensive inshore basin to unprecedented depths?

(iii) Would post-dredging tidal streams move bed material in the main dredged area, or on the marginal slopes, into the main channel in serious quantity?

 (iv) What would be the optimum post-dredging alignment of inshore dredged margins, and jetty head?

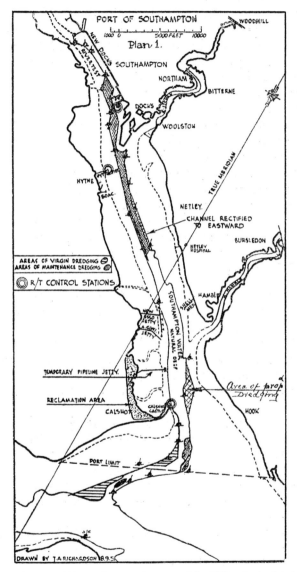

Fig. 1 Southampton Water, showing the areas of the 1950 main dredging contract and the proposed site under investigation (cross-hatched)

It was obvious that calculated theoretical values must be supported by the best positive confirmation that our present scientific knowledge could give, and I therefore decided to recommend the construction of a fixed-bed model by the Civil Engineering Department of Southampton University, to predict the post-dredging tidal stream regime at the proposed site.

I was fortunate in obtaining the assistance and collaboration of Dr. Wright, now Professor of Civil Engineering at Dublin University, whose experience in the construction of such models was extensive. His appreciation of the basic principles of the complicated local tidal behaviour outlined above ensured perfect and intimate collaboration in the tidal specification to which the model was constructed and operating within nine months, costs being borne by the petitioning company.

It was fully agreed that a fixed-bed model on suitable scales could, after satisfactory testing under present conditions, provide accurate predictions of post-dredging tidal streams after the dredged block was removed.

3. Tidal Specification for Translation and Model Terms

Accordingly the following tidal specification was agreed upon for translation into the model:

(i) The model must necessarily cover Southampton Water and the east and west Solent, and extend to the narrowest eastern and western hydraulic entrance sections, that is to Hurst narrows and Fort Gilkicker close westwards of Portsmouth entrance (Fig. 2).

(ii) A continuous spring tidal curve giving a 13.5-foot high water at Portsmouth would be employed to give maximum tidal rates.

(iii) The average daily tidal time cycle could, for this purpose, be expanded from 24.8 to 25 hours to simplify and cheapen mechanical gearing of the tide simulating mechanism.

(iv) The horizontal and vertical scales of the model would be $\frac{1}{1250}$ and $\frac{1}{100}$, respectively.

(v) The level datum of the model would be Ordnance Datum (Newlyn), all templates to be set to depths, and Admiralty

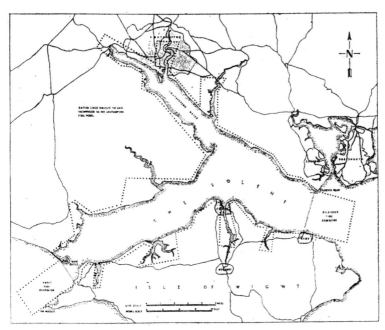

Fig. 2 The area encompassed by the Southampton tidal model is indicated by dotted lines

Chart datums defined by the charts of the area, namely, Nos. 1905, 394 and 2040, and the bottom in concrete so moulded: this involved about 40 benchmarks reproduced in the model.

(vi) Predicted tidal curves corresponding to the Portsmouth curve, as accepted in (ii) above, and correctly related to it, would be "fed" in at the eastern and western entrances, respectively, and the performance of the model would be governed by the resulting accuracy observed in the internal model phenomena, undisturbed by any artificial "adjustments" ("baffling," etc.) to induce conformity.

(vii) The following somewhat rigorous tests in *status quo* by the model were to be satisfied before predicted values for "post-dredging" results would be accepted:

(a) The accuracy in the heights of the model tidal curves produced by the above external tidal stimuli, in correct phase and time scale, should be within 2 per cent. of the range at Calshot and the Town Quay, respectively, and should reproduce substantially all their special features.

(b) The accuracy in the strength of the tidal streams at the site of investigation should be within 10 per cent. of observed values taken continuously over two spring periods.

(c) The accuracy in the direction of the dominant ebb tidal streams to be within 5 degrees of observed values.

(d) 20-foot continuous vertical submerged spar drifts at springs to conform generally on model scale to observed performance in the Solent axis and Southampton Water.

4. Model Time and Linear Scale Factors

The deduction of model scale factors for time and linear movement was as follows:

(i) Model time factor

$$= \frac{\sqrt{\text{Reciprocal of vertical scale}}}{\text{Reciprocal of horizontal scale}}$$

$$= \frac{\sqrt{100}}{1250} = \frac{1}{125}$$

i.e., one hour in natural scale $= 28.8$ secs. in model.
tidal cycle of 12.5 hours $= 360$ secs. $= 6$ mins.

(ii) Linear scale factor in model:

$$= \frac{1}{\sqrt{\text{Reciprocal of vertical scale}}}$$

$$= \frac{1}{\sqrt{100}} = \frac{1}{10}$$

i.e., 1 knot in nature $= 0.1$ knot in model.

It is, of course, necessary in such models that the vertical scale should be "exaggerated" as geometrical section would give a thin layer which, in view of friction, surface tension, etc., would be incapable of giving results corresponding to nature. Accordingly, a useful value is given by Lacey who considered that the "exaggeration" of vertical scale above natural should not seriously exceed the cube root of the reciprocal of the natural scale.

In the case of this model, this would give $\sqrt[3]{1250} = 10.8$. As the horizontal scale of the model was satisfactorily large, a value of 12.5 was considered reasonable by Dr. Wright. This judgment was amply confirmed by results.

The model was finally constructed and housed in a structure approximating an equilateral triangle of 120-foot sides.

5. Geological Prognosis for Nature of Transportable Material

While the work of construction, moulding, and housing of the model was proceeding, the company desiring local facilities was asked to make an extensive series of borings in good density at selected sites covering the area of the proposed dredging, down to a level of 40 feet below mean low water springs, to ascertain the horizon, depth and levels of the strata of transportable and loose material that might become exposed to movement in quantity after dredging.

A number of casual borings taken previously by other interests had revealed gravel and shingle strata at levels of about 30 feet below mean low water springs near this site.

Results showed that a stratum averaging 8 feet in thickness would be opened up by dredging to—37 feet at mean low water springs, but, very fortunately, the upper levels were nearly all below the proposed dredged levels, except, of course, on the inshore boundaries of the proposed area where adequate slopes would be necessary.

The actual material—shingle and gravel—varied from 1 inch-$2\frac{1}{2}$ inches in diameter, and was irregular and therefore not so liable to transportation as smooth weathered shingle, having formed a geological structure with Tertiary clays from Eocene times.

As bed rates of over 2 knots were dangerously near those theoretically required for the transportation of this material, it was decided to test samples in a "flume" to ascertain adequate boundary slope values for stability, and the results are shown in Fig. 3.

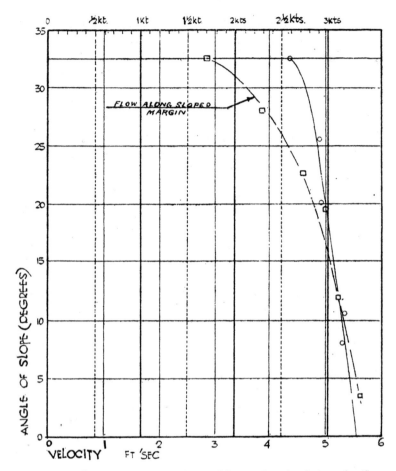

Fig. 3 The relationship between velocity of flow and angle of slope for flow over an inclined shingle bed (from Dr. Wright after flume tests)
———— O Flow down inclined plain　— — —□ Flow across inlined plane

6. Testing of Model by Existing Values for Tidal Streams

During the construction of the model a self-recording current meter of the latest pattern, made by Messrs. Kelvin Hughes, took continuous observations on the site being investigated for comparison with "pre-dredging" model indications. "Strong resolution" magnetic compass indications for direction at springs

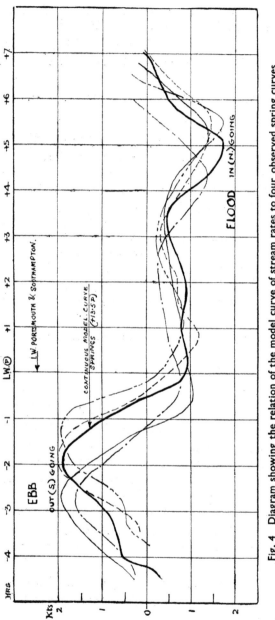

Fig. 4   Diagram showing the relation of the model curve of stream rates to four observed spring curves

were averaged, and corrected for local variation, giving the following values at dominant rates on flood and ebb:

	Model	Current Meter Mean of Means	20-foot Spar Drift at Maxima
On the flood:	307°	316°	309°
On the ebb:	132°	131°	134°

Directions are true—clockwise.

It will be noticed that current meter directions of "set," although limited by magnetic compass, and short "vane radius" (using a series of means at maximum rates of flood and ebb) are very satisfactorily close to model indications for the ebb. The flood direction, however, deviates by 9 degrees; but it should be pointed out that the spring flood rate, apart from a sharp peak at about 5 hours after low water (Portsmouth), is under 1 knot, and flood directions in nature are variable at differing ranges due to local contours and meteorological disturbance of normal levels at each entrance to the Solent. Fig. 4 compares model results with actual.

Model rates for maxima at the proposed jetty site were as follows:

	Model	Nature	
Ebb:	1.9	1.9	
Flood:	1.7	1.5	(Over 1 knot for only 1½ hours, with sharp peak of 20 minutes' duration).

The largest rate recorded in the model at the site of the proposed jetty head was 1.9 knots on the ebb, which was accepted in the light of the above confirmations, and the conditions for tidal stream accuracy set out in paragraph 3 (vii) (b) and (c) above were regarded as satisfactorily fulfilled in the model.

It should be stated that model rates were taken to represent 3 feet above the concrete bed, using the Wallingford miniature current meter.

It remains to demonstrate the agreement of the model with the other conditions of acceptance set out above in paragraph 3 (vii) (a) and (d).

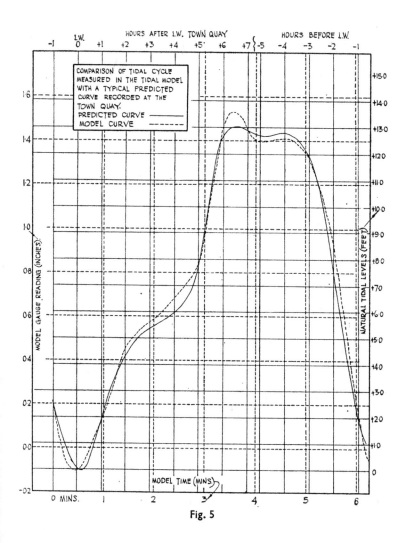

Fig. 5

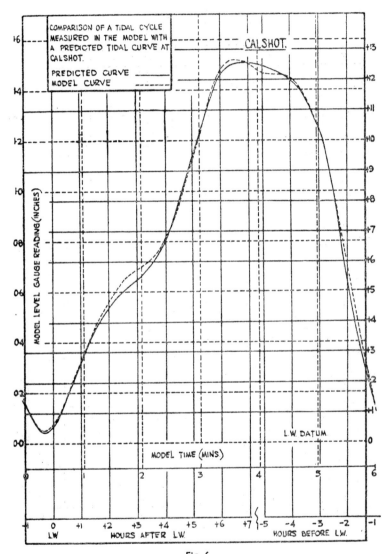

Fig. 6

7. Testing of Model by Reproduction of Curves of Heights

Regarding (a), the model curves for Calshot and the Town Quay showed a remarkable (and somewhat unexpected) identity with the predicted curve, well within the requirements, as shown in Figs. 5 and 6.

As the Calshot model curve showed an almost complete agreement with prediction, and was close to and representative of, the site being investigated, the situation was regarded by Dr. Wright and myself as highly satisfactory.

Regarding (d), the continuous spar drifts in the Solent and Southampton Water showed a reasonable agreement with some discrepancies, and it was accepted that these might be due to meteorological disturbances at each entrance of the Solent during the times of observation, together with range inequality and rather indeterminate frictional factors in the Solent, which would require a separate study.

The model was therefore considered to be a true hydraulic analogue *for the site under investigation.*

8. Relation of Post-Dredging Predictions to Transportable Material

Whilst the dredging block was in course of being removed from the model, flume tests of the material under consideration yielded the results shown in Fig. 3.

Figures given by Gibson (Hydraulics—Constable 1952, page 341) give the following data:

Material	Bottom Velocities, in feet per second, at which—		
	Transportation Begins	Material is in Equilibrium	Deposition Begins
Shingle—rounded, 1 inch or more in diameter	3.2 (1.9 knots)	2.14 (1.3 knots)	1.56 (0.93 knots)
*Flints—size of hen's egg	4.0 (2.4 knots)	3.2 (1.9 knots)	2.14 (1.3 knots)

*This would approximate in size to the material under consideration.

The figures given by the flume investigation for disturbance of representative material ("Transportation Begins" column in Gibson's Table) for flow parallel to a margin at varying slopes are as follows:—

Angle of Slope from Horizontal	Rate of Flow to Move on Bed (knots)	Using factor of 0.7 for Rate to Keep in Suspension (knots)
25°	2.55	1.8
20°	2.83	2.05
15°	3.00	2.10

These figures are larger than Gibson's, probably due to irregularity owing to lack of smoothing by weathering. It will be noted that bed rates required to move the material are well over the maximum post-dredging rates given by the model and that a reduction in slope increases the margin of safety.

9. Results of the Model Investigation

(i) The model was accepted as satisfactory for predicting hydraulic factors limited to the site being examined.

(ii) The agreed shape of the dredged area was regarded as reasonable for maintenance. No turbulence that might affect ship-handling appeared in the model, nor was any undue slackening of the stream discernible where the V^6 factor ratio indicate a tendency to deposit material in transport.

(iii) As the upper inshore dredged marginal slope had been designed in a 131 degrees to 311 degrees (true) direction and the model indications gave values of 133 degrees to 313 degrees at maximum rates, it was decided that it would be safe to align the seaward jetty head wharfage and dredged margin in accordance with model indications; that is to adjust the direction 2 degrees in a clockwise direction, thus saving 150,000-200,000 cubic yards (*in situ*) of dredging due to the investigation.

Fig. 7 shows the final adjustment reduced from a natural scale of 1/7500.

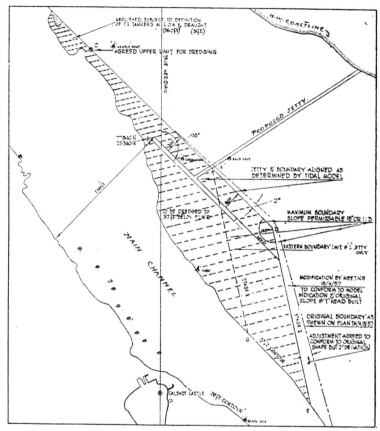

Fig. 7 The proposed dredging contract at Southampton

(iv) As maximum post-dredging bed rates, as determined by the model, would not exceed 2.1 knots, it was clear that under ordinary circumstances the sloping of the inshore dredged boundary to 25 degrees from the horizontal would require a bed rate of 2.55 knots to disturb the material on the bottom.

On the other hand, as the "fetch" from the West Solent might raise 3-foot *surface* waves, with prevailing south-westerly gales,

213

it was decided to specify a maximum dredged boundary slope of 20 degrees which raised the "equilibrium" speed for keeping disturbed material in suspension to 2.00 knots, which agrees with maximum model spring tidal rates, and reduces even this likelihood to a very small segment of the tidal cycle.

(v) The agreement of model determinations for vertical and horizontal tidal movement *at this particular site* enables a tidal album to be made covering positions in, and near, the proposed site in its post-dredging aspect for, say, every half-hour at springs, to determine the total regime of the streams encountered, for the benefit of navigators.

(vi) It was considered that dredging at the level of the shingle stratum should be timed to avoid the period when heavy south-westerly gales are likely.

10. Conclusions

The fixed-bed model principle, taken together with flume tests for rates affecting samples of the material, was capable of enabling a harbour authority to judge, with reasonable certitude, that the proposed dredging scheme was not likely to affect adversely the adjacent navigable fairway and approaches.

The enterprise of Southampton University, who have now taken over the model, and the initiative of the petitioning company, are, in my opinion, commendable in the extreme, and the project has been to the advantage of all concerned in dealing with the hydraulic aspect of this problem.

The value of a fixed-bed model for maximum tidal indications, using the approximations involved to expedite essential results, would seem to be well justified.

The Southampton Harbour Board have prepared a number of local studies where the guidance of model results will be of immense value in the near future.

In addition, it is fitting that the remarkable sea terminal areas in Southampton Water, with its incomparably favourable combination of tidal and other facilities, should provide our coming hydraulic engineering students with an experimental tidal area which poses a problem not yet fully solved by the greatest tidal experts in the world. The full solution of the tidal problem at Southampton will undoubtedly be one of the greatest achievements of science, and the construction of a model, such as that which has been made possible by the company desiring facilities, is an important step in this direction.

Finally, as a surveyor I must emphasise the paramount importance of obtaining *precise hydrographic field data* if such model results as I have described are to yield accurate conclusions, based upon correct premises.

For this purpose, well-qualified and experienced hydrographic surveyors are essential.

Furthermore, it is of the greatest importance that the resources of science should be applied to improving hydraulic instrumentation in all its applications, but particularly to the determination of the *direction* of tidal streams from surface to bed.

The hydrography of the Solent and Southampton water

INTRODUCTION

FROM ANCIENT times, the remarkable tidal regime observed in the waters behind the Isle of Wight has intrigued the sailors who found profit in braving the English Channel. Often driven up the Channel by the South-westerly gales that raise ocean waves against the south coast of England, they anxiously sought an entrance into the smoother waters of the Solent as a haven of refuge from such a deadly lee shore.

The various contributions to the formation of the present coastline—the Alpine folding, the creation of the English Channel and of the "Solent river," its dismemberment by the early Quaternary transgression, the separation of the Isle of Wight, the breaching of the southern Chalk ridge, wave erosion and shingle accretion are well known to geologists. These events in the geological history of the English Channel, and their results, have had profound effects on the unusually providential tidal phenomena which have made Southampton an obvious and unique terminal for the liners of today.

THE TIDAL PHENOMENA

The creation of the English Channel had two main hydrological consequences. These were (i) the progressive introduction of the semi-diurnal tidal pulse of the North Atlantic Ocean right into the Straits of Dover; and (ii) the opening of this converging gulf to the wave action of the ocean, with an immense "fetch," along which the prevailing westerly gales can raise wave amplitudes of 30 to 40 feet, with pressures of up to 5 tons per square foot.

If one regards the restricted area lying between Land's End and Dover as a "stationary wave compartment," with its own natural period of oscillation, one may roughly assume an average depth of 36 fathoms and a length of 300 miles. This resulting natural period of oscillation may be calculated from the following approximate formula*:

$$T = \frac{L}{4\sqrt{D}}$$

Where T = Period of natural oscillation in hours

       L = Length of compartment in nautical miles

      D = Depth (average) in fathoms.

Thus in this case: $T = \dfrac{300}{4\sqrt{36}}$

$$= \frac{300}{24}$$

$$= 12\tfrac{1}{2} \text{ hours.}$$

As this closely approximates to the diurnal tidal period of the Atlantic Ocean, it is clear that the English Channel is kept in continuous oscillation by the kinetic energy of the oceanic tidal pulse applied in perfect synchronism at the western entrance (Figs. III, 14 and 15).

A modern cotidal map of the English Channel (see Fig. III, 12) indicates the tidal regime which has prevailed since about 4500 B.C., when the outline of the English Channel had begun to assume its present shape. It has been shown that if one assumes a tidal compartment equal in length to the English Channel and with its average depth, the period of oscillation will coincide with the diurnal oceanic tidal oscillation at its western entrance off Land's End. This in itself is a phenomenal synchronism of natural forces, but it must, of course, be realised that this assumption is based on a uniform rectangular shape, and discrepancies from theory when the natural boundaries deviate

---

*This formula is derived from the standard formula for a standing oscillation —namely:

$$T = \frac{2l}{\sqrt{gh}}$$

Where T = period in seconds

      l = length in feet

      h = depth in feet

      g = acceleration due to gravity.

from the rectilinear are inevitable. If the English Channel were of uniform depth and truly rectangular in plan, one would expect no variation in vertical tidal level at the centre of its major axis or "node," but only an alternation of tidal stream movement during each period of oscillation ($12\frac{1}{2}$ hours). The transverse nodal line would run from somewhere near the western end of the Isle of Wight to the eastern side of the Cherbourg peninsula.

On the other hand, a glance at the map reveals a roughly converging Channel section, and the intrusion of the Cherbourg peninsula drastically reduces the cross-sectional area at that point. One must, therefore, expect the "node" to be unstable, due to the resistance to normal flow, which will, of course, be highest at the time of its greatest rate. Thus while the times of high water at Dover will coincide with those of low water at Land's End (and vice versa), one must expect deviation from theory over an area of instability, as shown in Fig. 1, and it would be reasonable to assume maxumim interference midway between the times of low and high waters (when tidal flow is

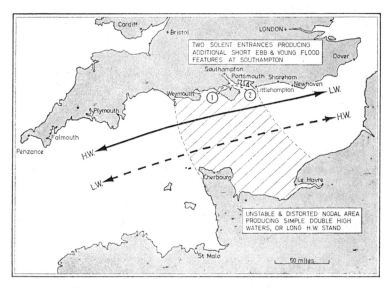

Fig. I   Degenerate nodal area in the English Channel

strongest)—that is, four times a day, i.e. of a quarter-diurnal nature.

It is well known that when the harmonic curves of a semi-diurnal (M_2) and quarter-diurnal (M_4) variety are combined, they will produce a double high water of an elementary character if the initial phase differences between the constituents are 180° or near (see Fig. III, 23). Fig. III, 7, showing synchronous tidal curves at Havre, Honfleur and Southampton, indicates that such a situation does occur across this section of the English Channel. It should, however, be noted that the duration of the ebb along the French coast is much longer than that of the flood, whereas the situation inside the Isle of Wight at Southampton reverses this relative duration. The reason for this will be discussed later. It is also interesting to note that where the M2 and M4 constituents start initially in phase (that is, where the latter is displaced by only three hours from the relation shown in the former example), double low waters result as in the case at Portland (see Figs. III, 9 and III, 24).

Two further phenomena can be noted from examination of the cotidal chart (see Fig. III, 12). In the first place, from its entrance to the English Channel, tidal undulation is normal (at right angles) to the Channel axis until its interruption by the Cherbourg peninsula, causing the elementary double high water produced in the manner described above. But the result of this asymmetrical construction of flow and convergence is to build up the range towards Dover, and to produce a large area lying eastward of a line joining Portsmouth Harbour entrance and Dieppe, over which the times of high waters are almost simultaneous. In the second place, tidal ranges tend to build up almost dramatically on the French coast. This is mainly a result of the earth's rotation (the Coriolis effect), which causes a deviation to the right of rectilinear motion in the northern hemisphere. This effect is accentuated by the obstruction to up-Channel flow provided by the Cherbourg peninsula, and it is notable that at St. Malo, Cancale and Granville the normal spring ranges (heights above low water) are $35\frac{1}{2}$, 44 and 43 feet respectively. By contrast, spring tidal ranges on the English coast, between Land's End and Dover, do not exceed 20 feet.

The Tidal Regime within the Isle of Wight

It is clear that while the formation of the English Channel provided an eastern entrance to the Solent, via the much widened section of the mouth of the old "Solent river" (see p. 48), the Chalk barrier across what is now the western inlet must have successfully resisted the intensive battering by storm-waves for a considerable time after the main marine transgression. The Needles still remain as a witness of such resistance, and the Bridge Reef farther to the west, probably the base of vanished stacks, has shown little evidence of substantial diminution over the last two centuries. Authorities vary as to the chronology of the final break-through, but it could have been as late as 3000 B.C.; some even place it still later.

While it has been shown that a pattern of simple double high waters has occurred over the "degenerate" nodal area (Fig. 1) since the formation of the English Channel, it is obvious that the tidal curves observed outside the Isle of Wight reveal remarkable divergences from those recorded at Calshot and Southampton, as can be seen from Fig. 2. For example, the Honfleur curve has a flood duration of only $2\frac{1}{2}$ hours, as compared with an ebb duration of 7 hours, and the Havre spring flood period occupies $4\frac{3}{4}$ hours, with the following ebb $6\frac{1}{2}$ hours.

To a seaman the longer the tide is standing or rising and the shorter the length of the ebb, the better he is pleased when navigating in shoal or harbour areas. The Southampton curve is indeed providential, and certainly exceptional, for it rises on the flood from low to high water at springs over a $6\frac{1}{2}$-hour period, with the remarkable interruption of a slack water stand lasting nearly two hours near Mean Tide Level, a phenomenon known locally as the "Young Flood Stand." In addition, the double high waters period following covers $1\frac{1}{2}$ hours, but the subsequent ebb occupies only $3\frac{3}{4}$ hours of the total $12\frac{1}{2}$-hour tidal cycle. These phenomena would not prevail if the eastern entrance to the Solent alone existed, for in such a case the situation outside the Isle of Wight would be more or less communicated to the Solent—namely, a short flood and a long ebb.

An examination of Fig. III, 26 shows that the tidal stream flowing within the Solent, with its two entrances, is not in phase with the tidal rise and fall outside the Isle of Wight. It is determined

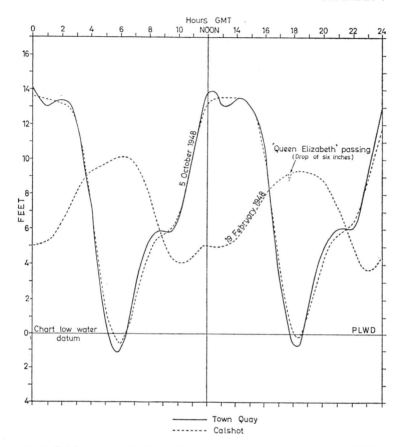

Fig. 2 Tidal curves at the Town Quay, Southampton and at Calshot. PLWD.
Port Low Water Datum (see Fig. 18)

by the varying hydraulic gradient prevailing at any given time
between the Needles and Spithead. Thus at spring high water,
which occurs at the Needles and Spithead within an hour of each
other, the semi-ranges (or heights above Mean Tide Level) are
3½ and 6½ feet respectively).

The tidal stream over the high water period must therefore
flow from east to west, the result of this 3-foot "head." The
reverse situation occurs at the time of spring low water, the
differences in ranges making the Needles low-water level about

3 feet above that at Spithead, causing an east-going stream in the whole Solent. When the Spithead level overtakes that at the Needles, as the tidal levels rise simultaneously at each end of the Solent, the direction of flow is reversed, following a very short period of slack water. There is little doubt that the existence of these two Solent entrances reverses the normal phase relation between the quarter-diurnal (M_4) and diurnal (M_2) tidal constituents, in such a manner as to cause long flood and short ebb periods, as well as the pause at the Young Flood Stand.

These secondary features of the Southampton phenomena are regarded as probably due to the two entrances to the Solent, with their hydraulic implications, and the sixth-diurnal tidal constituent is considered to be the feature to which some of the unique characteristics of the tidal curve are due.   It is instructive to note that the tidal model of the Solent and Southampton Water, constructed in 1958 for the Southampton Harbour Board, confirms this theory.

Summing up, it is abundantly clear that while simple double high-water phenomena prevail in the unstable area across the Channel between Portland and Chichester on the English side and Cherbourg and Dieppe on the French side (see Fig. III, 7), the remarkable tidal features shown in the Southampton tidal curve are undoubtedly due to modifications brought about the existence of two entrances to the Solent.

SOUTHAMPTON WATER

It is clear that a remarkable combination of natural features has favoured Southampton Water. These may be summarised as follows:

(i) The unique tidal regime, where for $8\frac{3}{4}$ hours the water level is either rising or standing, and the ebb lasts only $3\frac{3}{4}$ hours.

(ii) The "halt" on the flood tide in Southampton Water, occurring from $1\frac{3}{4}$ to $3\frac{1}{2}$ hours after low water, and averaging a useful level of from 1 to 2 feet below Mean Tide Level, with little horizontal tidal movement off the Docks, where such movement is in phase with changes in vertical tidal movement.

(iii) The protecting and sheltering barrier of the Isle of Wight.

(iv) The lay-out of Southampton Water in a south-easterly

direction across the dominant south-westerly direction of strong gales, with consequent freedom from powerful wave action. This feature has made Southampton Water a great attraction to ships of all sizes, seeking refuge from the storms of the English Channel, from pre-Roman times to the present. In addition, the short fetches result in freedom from wave erosion within Southampton Water. It is significant that the only wave-erosion occurs in the Hook area below the Hamble entrance, the result of west-south-westerly winds blowing over the maximum local fetch of 13 miles along the axis of the western Solent from the Needles Narrows off Hurst.

(v) The relatively small tidal range and the correspondingly small tidal streams in Southampton Water, which, while large enough to be useful, dispense with the need for lock-gates at the docks.

(vi) The incidence of dense fog in the Southampton and Calshot areas rarely exceeds an annual aggregate of 15 days. This value is considerably less than that prevailing even at the Needles entrance, or to the east of Spithead.

(vii) As the bed of Southampton Water and the Calshot submarine plateau was only recently submerged, the clays and gravels enable relatively permanent channels to be dredged easily as required to accommodate vessels of increasing draught (Figs. 3, 4). It is significant that there is no maintenance problem outside Calshot Castle, while the annual dredging programme of the thin alluvial "dressing" over the clays in the main channel between Fawley and the Dockhead does not involve more than 200,000 cubic yards.

An incidental feature of economic importance is the heavy accretion of shingle in the area immediately south-west of the Needles, forming around Pot Bank a submarine shoal area with a crest about six fathoms below Mean Low Water Springs. The combined effects of the relatively small tidal range outside the Needles, the long tidal stand and the continuous easterly movement of shingle on the bed of the English Channel, together with a northerly component (due to occasional strong southerly to south-westerly gales), result in a build-up and continuous supply of clean shingle at this site, with a corresponding wastage to the eastward. This phenomenon provides a source of valuable

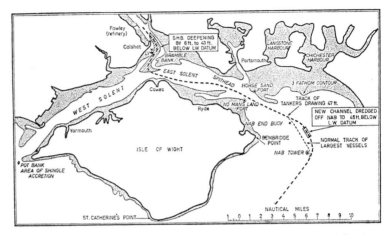

Fig. 3   Dredged channels off Calshot and The Nab.   Based on original drawings by the Southampton Harbour Board (S.H.B.)

building aggregate, now in increasing demand. A number of suction hopper dredgers (some constructed specifically for this purpose) are now exploiting this, and by the use of variable suction devices are able to select material of specified diameter immediately available for use.

(viii) The excellent holding-ground for anchoring the largest ships in the world is a special feature of Southampton Water and the Solent generally, where tenuous sticky clay is characteristic. The 17-ton anchor of the *Queen Mary* can enter for 5 to 6 feet below the sea-floor in such material with a tenacity that would part her 4-inch diameter cable before dragging.

(ix) The situation of the Solent, and especially Southampton Water, enables a large ship to avoid the tortuous routes, buoyed channels and long prevailing periods of poor visibility incidental to berthing at the ports of Liverpool, Bristol and London. Ships can arrive safely within the shelter of the Solent, half-way along the English Channel, where passengers and cargo are within easy reach of London.

HYDROGRAPHIC SURVEYS

Lord Kelvin once said that "science is measurement," and the science of hydrography is the precise measurement of all

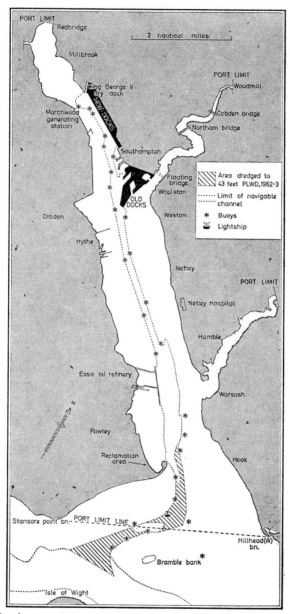

Fig. 4 Southampton Water based on the Southampton Harbour Board's map
(1952), with revisions.

the phenomena of submarine areas related to the safe passage and reception of the largest and deepest-draught ships using them. Scientific hydrographic surveys really commenced with Captain James Cook, R.N., during the eighteenth century, and some rather superficial work on the south-eastern coast of England was carried out by his redoubtable first lieutenant, Captain Bligh, after his unfortunate experience in H.M.S. *Bounty*. The development in the eighteenth century of Hadley's sextant made it possible for the first time to carry out accurate triangulation of the shore objects which must be available to control the accurate movement of the survey vessel, and enable it to plot its course and the position of the soundings it takes.

Lieutenant Murdoch McKenzie, R.N., made the first reaonably accurate survey of Southampton, both as to adjacent shore features and the positions and values of the soundings and contours. They are given on his plan dated 1783. Since that date, Admiralty charts presenting surveys of increasing detail of the Southampton and Solent areas have appeared with increasing frequency, especially after the "iron and steam" revolution which developed apace during the middle of the nineteenth century. It can be said, however, that the seaward limit of detailed soundings in estuarine areas and their approaches did not extend much beyond the 5-fathom contour; soundings in deeper waters were not necessary because of the light draught of ships, which did not exceed 20 feet for a long time. Moreover, the laborious method of sounding by lead and line made progress both difficult and slow.

The need for detailed surveys because of the increasing draught of ships has now extended beyond the 10-fathom contour. This requirement is met by the latest techniques of echo-sounding and of electronic devices for the accurate location of ships engaged in survey, developed over the last three decades, especially under the stimulus of the War of 1939-45.

MODERN DEVELOPMENTS IN SOUTHAMPTON WATER

The remarkable scientific advances of the last century included the change of ship construction from wood to steel, and, almost simultaneously, from sail to mechanical propulsion, with a correspondingly dramatic increase in the size of ships regularly plying the North Atlantic. Design, reflected in the increasing length and draught of such ships, is largely dependent upon the terminal facilities available, and, as has been shown, Southampton Water is most favourably situated. Under the aegis of Parliament, statutory powers were exercised by the Southampton Harbour Board in deepening and widening the approach channels, as the laying down of the keels of liners of ever increasing dimensions proceeded apace; the *Oceanic*, *Majestic*, *Teutonic* and *Adriatic* all made Southampton their European terminal in 1907. In 1909 the keels of the *Olympic* and the ill-fated *Titanic*, and soon after the *Aquitania* and the *Mauretania*, were laid. The approach channels to the Docks were accordingly deepened from 30 to 35 feet below Mean Low Water Springs between the years 1893 and 1913. Between the two World Wars further widening and deepening proceeded, notably in preparation for the *Queen Mary* in 1936. The favourable nature of the bed of Southampton Water and its approaches from the Solent is reflected in the uniquely low maintenance dredging requirements already stressed.

In 1950 further dredging was undertaken in the approaches to Southampton and the Docks, the spoil amounting to $3\frac{1}{2}$ million cubic yards. On this occasion the Calshot Spit was shaped to a 4000-foot radius curve to fit the turning tracks in shallow water of the Cunard *"Queens,"* each over 1000 feet in length. These vessels can now negotiate what used to be a dangerously acute turn with relatively small easy helm (5° to 10°) and no requirements of drastic engine assistance. The berm, or dredged margin, of the new curve (composed of clay, gravel and shingle) has retained its dredged contours.

The largest project ever for dredging the bed of the Solent off the Nab and Calshot commenced in 1962, where it was required to accommodate tankers of over 100,000 tons displacement and drawing 47 feet at the Fawley installation. Model tests at the National Physical Laboratory (Teddington) indicated that in shallow approach channels these vessels would trim by the head, and increase draught by as much as 3 to 5 feet at speeds of 10 to 12 knots respectively. Accordingly, the requirements aimed at providing dredged channels 45 to 43 feet below Mean Low Water Springs off the Nab and off Calshot respectively (Fig. 3). The problem was to determine whether the large flints and shingle, 2 to

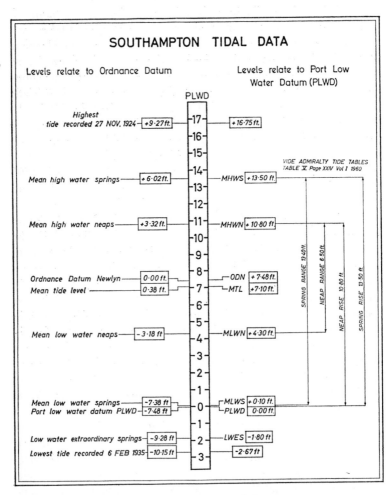

Fig. 5 Southampton tidal data
Based on (i) *Admiralty Tide Tables*, Vol. I, Table V, p. xxiv (London, 1960);
(ii) Southampton Harbour Board records.
The Hydrographer of the Navy has decided to lower the Port Low Water Datum
by 1.5 feet as from 1 January 1965

3 feet thick, covering a hard sand base in the Nab Channel, would remain stable after dredging to the specified depth, in view of the large swell values of up to 10 feet in strong winds, rising to values of 12 to 15 feet during exceptional southerly gales over the 90-mile fetch from the French coast. Fortunately, the rotary anti-clockwise tidal streams prevailing at the site naturally favoured the project after the channel had been deepened beyond 50 per cent of the required sectional area. The annual accretion, estimated as being less than 500,000 cubic yards, was accepted as being within economic limits for the maintenance costs involved in operating the 1500-foot wide channel. Subsequent surveys have much reduced this estimate.

Accordingly, as the Nab investigation proved favourable, the approach channels leading from the Solent off Calshot to the Fawley installation were depeened by 6 feet below their present bed level, to 43 feet below Port Low Water Datum (Fig. 5). This bottom level now gives depths at high water of 55 and 53 feet at springs and neaps respectively; the work was completed in August 1963.*

It is certain, however, that the exhaustion of marine possibilities in the Solent and Southampton areas is not yet in sight. Notwithstanding the demanding pressures of the twentieth century, the ideal concentration of varied natural features here provide an ocean terminal towards which science and technology must increasingly devote their attention and direct their skills.

---

*The first large tanker, *Esso Lancashire* (drawing 47 feet 5 inches), arrived at the Fawley Marine Terminal on 29 August 1963, bringing 78,300 tons of crude oil from Marsa el Brega, Libya.

BIBLIOGRAPHICAL NOTE

(1) A. T. Doodson and H. D. Warburg—*Admiralty manual of tides* (London, 1941), pp. 224-6.
(2) R. C. H. Russell and D. H. Macmillan—*Waves and tides* (London, 1952).
(3) *The Channel pilot*, Vol. I (14th edition, London, 1957), especially pp. 204-27.

Symbols used

A   Area.

b   Breadth or width, also tidal angle in Admiralty method of prediction.

C   Wave velocity.

c   Moon's angle.

D   Depth below mean tide, sea or water level in fathoms

d   Distance.

e   Radius of the earth.

E   Mass of the earth.

F   Fall in water level between two stations.

f   force.

g   The co-efficient of gravitational force. (Also used conventionally for phase lag in harmonic prediction).

h   Depth or height as stated.

H   Height of wave or tidal constituent above mean sea, tide or water level. Also hydraulic "Head" where stated.

K   Speed in knots.

L   Wave-length of free oscillation. Sometimes λ. Sometimes lengths in n.m.

l   Length. In astronomical formulae—latitude.

m   Mass of a particle.

n   Speed of harmonic tidal constituent in degrees per hour.

P   Wetted perimeter of channel cross-section.

p   Corrected barometric pressure of height in inches.

R   Tidal range (sometimes rise in level). Occasionally Hydraulic Radius.

r   Distance of moon from the centre of the earth, or generally radius.

t or

T   Period of time.

V   Velocity of particle. Sometimes v.

ω Angular velocity of earth's rotation.

y   Elevation of surface above mean tide, sea, or water level.

N.B.   These symbols are sometimes varied in loco. as indicated.

Conversion chart

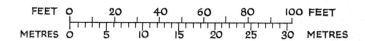

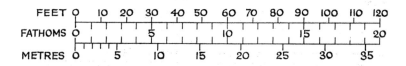

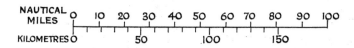

Index Glossary

Reference to topics of the Bibliographies are included.
A hyphen means that references to the topic are on all the pages covered.

Geneva, Lake, 119, 120
geoid, 138
geophysics, 179
Gibson, Professor, A. H., 184
gravity, 16, 17, 18, 26, 28, 31, 32, 48, 49, 183
——centre of, 133
Greeks, 11, 12
grunion, 151 - 153, 171
Gulder, the, 64, 67
gulf, 76, 113, 118, 121, 124
gyroscopic compass, 180
——effect (deflection of water particles in motion, to the right in the N. and to the left in the S. hemispheres reducing nodal lines to amphidromic points, around which co-tidal lines rotate anti-clockwise in N. and clockwise in S. hemispheres), 21, 72, 81, 82, 122 - 124, 127, 147, 180
gyroscopic force, 80, 81

H.W.F. & C. High Water full and change, 20, 71
H.W.I. High Water lunitidal interval
Halley, 17
harbours, 97, 111, 112, 132, 139, 140, 142 - 144, 160, 162, 171
harmonic, 22, 49 - 55, 88, 89, 90, 91, 92, 93, 97, 102 - 104, 108, 140, 146, 167 - 169, Appendix III
——constituents of constants (divisions of species of tides combining harmonically to produce an actual tide, given in amplitude ratio or height in feet, and phase lag in degrees for each constituent)
Harris, 147
head of water, 164 - 166, 174
Heiberg, 25
height, see wave height, 20
heliocentric, 16
Herodotus, 12
high water full & change (interval between the moon's midnight transit on days of full and new moon and the following high water, (at the time of high-water of the days of full and change where the tide is semi-diurnal or synodic)
high water lunitidal interval (time between moon's transit across the local meridian and culmination of tide at next high water)

——(maximum height of tide referred to datum no-tide level), 99, 106, 111, 121, 125 - 126, 142, 151 - 152, 167
Himilco, 12
horizontal component, 32
——plane, 105
horse-power H.P., 173, 175, 176
hydraulic radius, 155, 156, 158
hydraulics, 19, 21, 22, 23, 60, 94, 95, 124, 127, 143, 146, 165, 172
Hydrographer of Navy, 167
Hydrographic Conference, International, 137
——Department of British Admiralty, 24, 109
——Office, U.S., see U.S.

Ice, 144
Iceland, 48
Inglis, Sir Claude, 171
instruments, see recorder
inundation, 207
isobars, 181

John King, 14
Johnstone, 30, 51, 56

Kaplan turbine, 175
Kelvin, 22, 24, 49, 167
Kepler's Law, 46

L.W.F. & C. Low Water full and change, 20
L.W.I. Low Water lunitidal interval
Lag, 39, 40, 46, 50 103, 108, 166
land survey plane, 99, 102, 105
Laplace, 22, 25, 49
latitude, 41, 81, 122, 123
lift of wreck, 172, 173
lightship, 100
live water, 12
Liverpool Bench Mark, 138
——Tidal Institute, 112, 120, 147, 167, 181 - 183,
locks, 142, 143, 145
log-ship; see float, 133, 135
long period tidal oscillations (all tides with periods ranging from half a lunation 14 days, to the metonic cycle of 19 years)
low pressure disturbance, 115
——water interval (related to moon's transits, as are high water intervals where the tides are semi-diurnal), 12, 13, 16, 17, 24, 37, 38, 44, 46, 48, 72, 81, 87, 97, 106, 111, 121, 167

Date Due